EVOCAT

TALES

Stories and Legends from Bristol

Paul Hatch

Illustrations and photographs by Paul Hache

FIRST PUBLISHED IN GREAT BRITAIN IN 2011 BY:

Diesel Publishing
2 The Tithe Barn
High Street
Hawkesbury Upton
South Gloucestershire
GL9 1AY

dieselpublishing@fsmail.net

www.dieselpublishing.com

ISBN 978-0-9554455-5-2

Printed and bound in Great Britain by Henry Ling Limited
The Dorset Press

Stories and Legends from Bristol

The Kinsale Giant	5
The Annual Fairs	11
Whiteladies Road	12
Blackboy Hill	14
Cook's Folly	15
The Legend of Avalon, Vincent and Goram	18
The Story of Sabrina	21
Tombstone of Mystery	22
The Veiled Lady	23
The Blackness	26
Princess Caraboo	28
The Story of Mary Wilcox	40
The Curse of Rebecca Berjew	50

The Kinsale Giant

In November 1779 the *Lady Fitzgerald*, a small trading ship out of Cork in Ireland entered the Port of Bristol and was tied up at the Quay near the Assembly Room. All along the waterfront the quay-labourers were busy moving cargo that had been brought in aboard other ships but most of the labourers stopped to stare in amazement when they saw something they could hardly believe. Stepping on to the quay from the Irish vessel was a giant of a man who stood in excess of eight feet in height and towered over the labourers, most of whom were no more than the average height of about 5'6". Many townspeople watched in disbelief as the giant strolled along the Quay and into Clare Street where he entered the home of the watchmaker, Mr Safford. A giant of this colossal size had never been seen by any of the townspeople before – but *who* was he and why had he come to Bristol? These questions were on many people's lips but they didn't have long to wait before the answers were revealed.

The giant's name was Patrick Cotter and he was a staggering 8'3" tall, proportionately wide and weighed 25 stone. He had been born of poor parents in Kinsale, County Cork in 1760 and brought up as a bricklayer and a general labourer. But with the promise of fame and fortune he had leased himself to a would-be showman for three years at a wage of £50 per year. Soon after he came to Bristol he added the stage-name of O'Brien after his surname in the manner of Irish giants. He claimed to be a lineal descendant of the great Irish hero, Brian Boru (926-1014), and to have "*in his person and appearance all the similitude of that great and grand potentate.*" He said he was also proud to be of the company of other Irish giants such as Fingal, Ossian, Long Mores, and Charles Byrne. So, with his first show-appearance in Bristol, the exhibition career of Patrick Cotter O'Brien began.

In a large room in the back of Mr Safford's shop the giant was to meet members of the public who were invited to see him for a fee of one shilling per person. However, his stay in Bristol was to be short for under the direction of his showman-employer Cotter was to leave Bristol at the end of November to visit other towns and cities throughout the country. That was the plan but due to his great popularity he remained in Bristol until the end of December. Then just before they were about to leave, a dispute arose between Cotter and his employer when the showman attempted to sublet the right to exhibit Cotter to another agent. This agreement meant that no monetary allowance would be made to Cotter and he would only receive his food, clothing and lodgings. Because Cotter refused to go along with this he was falsely accused of debt by the showman and committed to the Bristol sponging house (the debtors prison).

In great distress, Cotter remained in prison until early in 1780 when a prominent Bristol citizen named William Watts, a hosier of 24 High Street, turned up at the sponging house in Taylor's Court to visit a friend. Soon after entering the building he notice that in a dark corner of the room there sat an enormous man who was sobbing miserably. Watts asked his friend who the man was and he told him that the man's name was Patrick Cotter. He said that Cotter had sold himself to the captain of an Irish trading ship from Cork. The captain fancied himself as a showman, by which means he hoped to make a lot of money. But a dispute arose between Cotter and the captain when the captain, who wanted to return to his ship, tried to sell his rights in Cotter to a genuine showman. When Cotter refused to work for this new employer the captain swore a debt against him.

Watts, who was a compassionate man, took pity on Cotter and paid the bail for his release. He took him to a tavern called the Jolly Brewers in the Temple Street area where he was fitted out with a redcoat and waistcoat trimmed with gold, a large gold-laced hat and breeches fastened at the knees over long silk stockings. A few weeks later he was exhibited to the public at the long established Temple Fair. On a canvas banner was painted the words, *'The Irish Giant – the lineal descendant of the old and puissant King Bryan Boreau – near nine feet high.'* This was an exaggeration of course but crowds flocked to see him for Patrick Cotter had now become well known and very well liked in Bristol because of his gentle and polite manner. He was paid well for his appearances and from his takings he gave the sum of one guinea to Mr Watts to book the drawing room of the Jolly Brewers for all future Temple fairs. A condition of this contract was that the name of the Jolly Brewers should be changed to the Giant's Castle.

Cotter (now working for himself instead of for a showman) began to travel around the country frequenting many of the great fairs of England. After an appearance at Bristol's Corn Exchange he went to London and showed himself in a room at the Haymarket, claiming in his advertisements descent from Irish kings of gigantic size. His average earnings, when in London, were a massive £10 a day. With some of this money he purchased his own carriage, which was specially constructed with a low foot-well section in the floor to take his large legs and size 15 shoes. He was so large that everywhere he went he had to sleep on two double beds placed together. He often walked the streets at night when it was quiet so as to avoid the crowds who had not paid to view him, and when strolling around at night he loved to smoke his pipe and would often light it by taking the tops off the seven-foot high oil lamps illuminating the streets. Once, for a wager and to show people just how tall he really was, he kissed a pretty girl who was leaning out of an upper window at her abode in Cheapside. His appetite was also huge and he ate four large steaks for his dinner each day together with vegetables, a score of eggs and three quartern loves washed down with three quarts of beer.

Cotter visited many towns and cities throughout the country but no matter how much he travelled, he always considered Bristol to be his home and returned to this city at the end of each fair-season. When he was here he spent

many afternoons at the Artichoke or the Ben Johnson Porterhouse, Under the Bank (now Saint Augustine's Parade) where he could relax, smoke his pipe and play cards. He was also a frequent visitor to the theatre where he always sat with his back against a partition so as not to obstruct the view of any of the patrons. Cotter went back to Ireland at the end of the 1782 fair-season and returned to Bristol in June the following year. During the voyages he had to sleep on deck because there was no bunk big enough to hold him. On 19th July 1783 a bill was posted advertising '*the arrival from Ireland of Patrick O'Brien of that kingdom.*' He could now be seen at Mr Shenstone's tavern, the Full Moon on North Street, Stokes Croft, by permission of the Mayor. He remained in this area for many weeks and appeared at several different addresses during August ending up at the house of a Mr Williams of the Horsefair.

During one of his tours, Cotter was on his way from London to Windsor in his carriage when his driver was stopped by a highwayman; who demanded money. When Cotter put his head out of the window to see why the driver had stopped, the highwayman was so shocked at the sight of this giant that he turned his horse and galloped away as fast as he could. In 1794 Cotter toured South Wales for the first time, passing through Ross before travelling on to Monmouth. He appeared in London at Sadler's Wells and at St Bartholomew's Fair but in 1801 he withdrew from public life after just a few appearances. This led to a rumour that he had died and there was no further record of him there until he returned to the London Haymarket three years later. But in the mean time, on 6th March 1802, Cotter arrived at the abode of a Mr Roach in Temple Street, Bristol. Here he could be seen at the Temple Fair where Cotter took the opportunity to quash the rumours of his death. At the end of March he made an appearance in Bath at the Angel Inn, Westgate Street. Having assured the people of Bristol and Bath that he was still alive, he travelled to Edinburgh via Nottingham where, in 1803, the artist John Kay drew his portrait.

He became so wealthy that he was able to buy several houses, which he purchased from his great fortune accumulated from showing himself. One of his homes was in Epping Forest where he spent much of his time when he was not exhibiting. Formerly the mansion of a noble family this building had later been converted into an inn before falling into disuse. The house was very suitable for someone of Cotter's stature because it had tall doorways and high ceilings in every room. The house was in the care of a widow for whom Cotter made many transactions in the purchase and sale of horses. In 1804, soon after his London Haymarket exhibition, Cotter retired from the showground circuit although he remained for a while at his abode in Epping Forest before selling it and returning to Bristol.

During his 30s Cotter's physical state had deteriorated considerably and by the age of 40 he found it difficult to walk. His legs had become swollen and weak and his arms seemed to wither and became unable to properly support his massive hands. When walking in the street at 2 or 3 o'clock in the morning he rested his arms on two of his companions, who were of normal size, and he would shuffle rather than walk as if he were unable to lift his feet. It seems that his spine was also compacting because his true height, although never accurately measured, seemed to have reduced to about 7'10". He stopped growing soon after he reached the age of 25 when his height was said to have been 8'7" – the tallest man ever to be exhibited in England. By the time he was 40 his hands were 12" wide and his face and lower jaw had grown extremely large in proportion to the rest of his body.

He retired to Hotwells at the end of 1804 and it was here that he made his will shortly before his death two years later. The Catholic priest, Father Plowden attended Cotter's final moments, but fortunately Cotter seems to have passed away peacefully without any pain or discomfort. The cause of his death was recorded as "An infection of the lungs combined with an affection of the liver." From this it is assumed that he died from a tubercular condition that was common to people of his stature. He died at the age of 46 in the Mardyke Tavern on Hotwell Road (the home of Joseph Francis) on 8th September 1806. He was buried in the old Jesuit Chapel in Trenchard Street and a marble tablet to his memory was placed in the chapel lobby, inscribed:

HERE LIE
THE REMAINS OF
MR. PATRICK COTTER O'BRIEN
A NATIVE OF KINSALE
IN THE KINGDOM OF IRELAND.
HE WAS A MAN OF GIGANTIC STATURE
EXCEEDING 8 FEET 3 INCHES IN HEIGHT
AND PROPORTIONATELY LARGE.
HIS MANNERS WERE AMIABLE AND UNOFFENDING
AND THE INFLEXIBLE INTEGRITY OF HIS CONDUCT
UNITED TO THE CALM RESIGNATION WITH WHICH
HE AWAITED THE APPROACH OF DEATH
PROVED THAT HIS PRINCIPLES
WERE STRICTLY VIRTUOUS.
HE DIED AT THE HOTWELLS
ON THE 8TH SEPTEMBER 1806
IN THE 46TH YEAR OF HIS AGE.

REQUIESCAT IN PACE

Cotter's coffin was 9'5" long and so broad that five ordinary men could lie in it together on their sides. The brass plate upon it was inscribed 'Patrick Cotter O'Brien of Kinsale, Ireland, whose stature was eight feet four inches, died 8th September 1806, aged forty-six.'

In life, Cotter had a great horror of his body getting into the hands of surgeons or his corpse exposed to public view by showmen. He gave directions for his funeral so as to ensure that his body would always "rest in peace." His coffin was lowered into a deep vault cut into the sandstone rock and above it he requested upwards of a ton of iron bars to be embedded in cemented masonry. But not long after Cotter's burial many people in Bristol began to hear of the existence of a giant's skeleton, 8'3" in height at the Museum of the Royal College of Surgeons in London. It was suggested that Cotter's body might have been removed from the coffin immediately before the funeral, but the London surgeons insisted that their skeleton was that of the giant Charles Byrne who died at the age of about 21. Byrne also sometimes called himself O'Brien so, the surgeons said, the Bristol giant's skeleton was certainly not the one that appeared in the London museum. But the belief by many that the London museum skeleton really was that of Cotter persisted for 100 years until the reconstruction of the Jesuit Chapel in 1906 led to the discovery of Cotter's skeletal remains buried ten feet below the foot of a staircase leading to the organ gallery.

The discovery was made by workmen who were laying drains ready for the conversion of the chapel into a school-hall – which was to become known as St Joseph's Hall. It was decided that the remains of Cotter would be re-interred, but before they were, permission was granted for the examination and measurement of the bones to be carried out by Professor Edward Fawcett of the Bristol University College and Mr Bolton, the curator of the City Museum. From these examinations it was estimated that Cotter's height when he died was about 7'10". There was malformation of the skull with massive enlargement of the *sella turcica* (the cavity housing the pituitary gland) indicating increased glandular activity, which is associated with gigantism. The enormous size of his hands showed that Cotter also suffered from acromegaly, a medical condition that causes people's hands, feet and face to grow to gigantic size. Even at 7'10" Cotter's height was exceptional for the late 18th century, but even today the anatomical definition of a giant is a man who stands more than 6'6½" in height and a woman who exceeds 6'2½", so Cotter was certainly a giant among giants.

In December 1972 further modifications were made to St Joseph's Hall and Cotter's bones were once again removed for a more thorough examination, this time by a Dr Jonathan Musgrave. On completion of the work at the hall in 1973 Cotter's bones were re-interred in a specially made casket in the vault from which they had been taken.

The Annual Fairs

From the 15th to the 19th centuries many of the towns and cities of Britain had an annual fair of the type frequented by Cotter. In Bristol there were two fairs, which were famous throughout the land as being among the largest and the best. The larger and greater of the two was St James's Fair, which commenced on 1st September and was held in the spacious grounds of St James's churchyard. Temple Fair began on 1st March and was held in and around Temple Street.

These fairs had numerous stalls where vendors sold all manner of goods. There were exhibitions of wild beasts and street entertainment such as tumbling and wire-dancing as well as puppet shows such as Mr Punch and his wife Joan (later to become known as Punch and Judy). Throughout the fairground there could be seen conjuration and magic, buffoons and mummery and people playing drums, trumpets, fiddles and rattles. They were noisy, rowdy events where honest people mixed with thieves and vagabonds. Cutpurses and pickpockets were everywhere and drunken louts were always ready for a fight. But for the most part they were happy occasions where people went to enjoy themselves and purchase things they wouldn't normally have a chance to buy. There was also food of many kinds including pies and hot muffins, roast ox and succulent goose.

Whiteladies Road

During the 17th and 18th centuries the slopes from Durdham Down (below what is now Upper Belgrave Road) was covered with a network of lanes and winding pathways lined with rural cottages. At the end of one of those lanes (near the eastern end of what is now Apsley Road) stood the White Ladies Tavern, which was built in 1610. The road leading north from Bristol to the villages of Westbury-on-Trym and Stoke Bishop passed by this tavern and many people who travelled along this highway used the tavern for refreshments and to water their horses. This led to the road being called White Ladies Road for it was the tradition for some streets to be named after taverns located along their length.

During the 1740s and 50s the landlord of the tavern was a retired seaman named Thomas Symonds who lived there with his wife and a servant girl named Mary Wiltshire who was affectionately known as Molly. She started working at the tavern in 1747 when she was 11 years old and was such a beautiful girl that she became a great favourite with the men, both young and old, who stopped at the tavern on their way to and from Bristol. Mr Symonds also took in lodgers at the White Ladies Tavern and one of these was a Swedish seaman named Joseph Abseny who was in his early 40s. Soon after he moved in (early in 1749) he began to flirt with Molly and started giving her little gifts. As she was now 13 years old this was quite acceptable because it was a time when girls could marry at the age of 12 and boys at the age of 14. However, it wasn't long before Molly grew tired of Abseny's advances, but when she told him that she didn't want anything more to do with him he became very angry and verbally abusive. Molly tried to ignore this and under the protection of Mr and Mrs Symonds she continued with her duties.

A few weeks later, on a warm sunny July day, Mrs Symonds sent Molly to the nearby Blackamoor's Head to buy 3 lbs of butter because she was running low. Molly left by the back door but a few minutes later Abseny went rushing out after her. Mrs Symonds didn't take much notice of this but after more than an hour had passed (and Molly had not returned) Mrs Symonds became worried and asked her husband to go and look for her. On the hill near the Blackamoor's Head a neighbour told Mr Symonds that she had seen Abseny dragging Molly by the arm, up towards Durdham Down. When Symonds reached the top of the hill he was shocked to find the mutilated body of Molly laying in a pool of blood. She had been stabbed many times with a knife and one knife wound to her neck was so deep that it had gone right through to the other side. She had obviously tried to defend herself from the attacker by holding her hand up in front of her face because one of her fingers had been completely severed and was lying on the ground. Her attacker had obviously cut himself very badly as well because there was a trail of blood leading from the scene along the road to Stoke Bishop.

Thomas Symonds quickly formed a posse of men from the village and they followed the trail of blood across the Downs, all the way to Sea Mills and Hungroad on the River Avon. Here they found that Abseny had been rowed out to a ship called the *Sheerness*, which was bound for Cadiz in Southern Spain. Due to the fact that the tide was out, the ship was still tied up waiting to depart. With no way to escape, Abseny was captured and held in chains until he could be taken to Gloucester for trial. Full of remorse he pleaded guilty and was brought back to Bristol to be hanged on Durdham Down near the spot where he had so brutally murdered Molly. Life at the White Ladies Tavern was never the same after that, and when the landlord died in 1761 the tavern fell into disuse and was demolished very soon after.

But why was this tavern called White Ladies? There is a story, which tells that the tavern was built on the site of a tumbledown cottage that was previously occupied by a young couple that went to live there in the 1520s. They had seven children, all of them girls, who were born in this cottage and lived there throughout their entire lives. None of these sisters ever married and each one died a virgin in old age. They always dressed in white, with white dresses, white aprons and white bonnets. Because of this they became known to everyone in their community as the White Ladies. They were very friendly and helpful to all their neighbours and would do anything they could if their friends were in need or in trouble.

Unfortunately they were so poor that they didn't have any money and when the first of them died her sisters were unable to pay for a funeral. Because of this the neighbours took the body up to the common land on Durdham Down and buried her there. But because there was no headstone, one of the neighbours planted a sapling at the head of the grave to mark its location. The remaining sisters, unable to purchase black dresses, had to continue wearing white to mourn the one that was lost. As this was not the tradition the six sisters became very upset and in their grief they slowly pined away. Within two years they had all died and the bodies of each was laid to rest in the same little area on Durdham Down. A sapling was planted at the head of each grave and over the following years they grew into tall pine trees.

During a storm one night the wind howled through the branches in such a way that it sounded like distant voices singing. A group of travellers passing by on their way to Bristol heard this sound and two little children asked what it was. Their mother told them it was a song being sung by the seven sisters and from that moment the trees themselves became know as the Seven Sisters. Today there are only three of them remaining but soon these trees will be gone as well. But from the seven sisters who were know as the White Ladies came the name of the tavern that was built on the site of their cottage – and from this tavern came the name we know today as, Whiteladies Road.

Blackboy Hill

Another tavern was built on the hill alongside the road to Westbury-on-Trym, this one during the reign of King Charles II (1660-1685). This tavern took its name from the king, not as the King's Head as later taverns might have been, but as the Blackamoor's Head. Charles II had a very swarthy complexion and blackamoor was a name given to anyone with dark or swarthy skin. During the early 19th century the name of this tavern was changed to the Black Boy Inn and from this came the name Black Boy Hill. However, this name still referred to King Charles II.

During the 20th century a story began to spread among the people of Bristol inferring that the tavern was connected in some way to the Bristol merchants involvement in the African slave trade. Some people even suggested that black slaves were brought here to be sold and were chained to the walls outside the tavern. This is untrue for African slaves were never brought in to Bristol. The only Africans who were brought here to work were indentured servants and there were very few of those. Rings on the wall outside the tavern were there for the purpose of tying up horses, not for tying up African slaves.

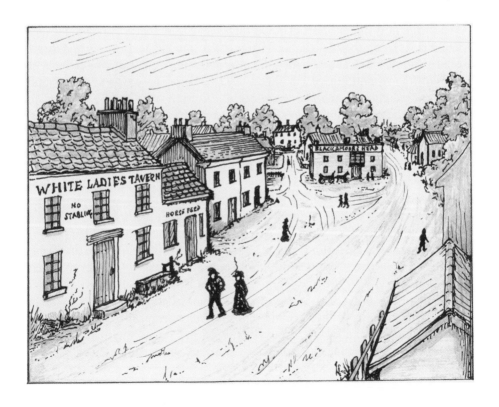

Cook's Folly

There have been many follies built throughout Britain and they were usually constructed for the purpose of keeping the name of a self-important person for posterity. These buildings were often fantastic, expensive erections built upon high places and occasionally left incomplete. But not all of them were buildings for some were constructed underground as elaborate and highly decorated grottos. Cook's Folly however, was a tall tower built and paid for by John Cook, merchant of Bristol who was Sheriff of the city in 1672. The door lintel bore the inscription, *J Cook 1693*. Demolished in 1932, the folly was a simple, hexagonal tower that stood on Knoll Hill overlooking the River Avon at Stoke Bishop. But this folly had a purpose for it seems that Cook wanted a retreat from the bustle of the city and to have an observatory from which he could view his beautiful surroundings.

After Cook's death the tower became shrouded in mystery and legend, which grew and developed over many generations. Like most legend, this one had several variations but the most popular of these seems to have originated in Egypt and comes from a mutilated papyrus, which is now held in the British Museum. It tells of a Pharaoh's son for whom sudden death by means of a crocodile or serpent was foretold. What eventually happened to the son is unknown for the last part of the manuscript is missing. The most popular version of the Cook's Folly legend is as follows:-

The wife of Sir Maurice Cook, Lord of the Manor of Stoke Bishop, was expecting her first child. One evening, while strolling alone in the grounds of their estate, the woman was accosted by a strange looking Romany man. He asked Lady Cook for some money and she gave him a coin saying, "That's all I have but it should be enough to buy you food for the present – so please go now and leave me to continue my walk in peace."

But the man was not satisfied and he asked for more. He said he was an astrologer to whom the heavens were as familiar as a book and that he could tell fortunes and read human destinies. He was so persuasive that Lady Cook fetched some more money and, her curiosity aroused, asked the man to predict the fate of her unborn child.

The Romany man looked deep into her eyes for a few seconds and then he said, "Note the exact moment when the baby enters the world. Soon after that you will hear from me again."

Six days later a son was born and was given the name of Walter. Within the hour the stranger appeared at the door and a servant told him the precise time of the baby's birth. The stranger hurriedly walked away but the next day he returned and presented the proud father with a small scroll on which was written the following words:

Twenty times shall Avon's tide
In chains of glistening ice be tied –
Twenty times the woods of Leigh
Shall wave their branches merrily,
In spring burst forth in mantle gay
And dance in summer's scorching ray,
Twenty times shall autumn's frown
Wither all their green to brown –
And still the child of yesterday
Shall laugh the happy hours away.
That period past, another sun
Shall not his annual journey run,
Before a silent, secret foe
Shall strike that boy a deadly blow.
Such and sure his fate will be,
Seek not to change his destiny.

Sir Maurice, who believed in astrology, read the lines with horror. He was so disturbed by them that he decided not to show the scroll to his wife. But as time passed the memory of the incident faded from his mind. Although Lord and Lady Cook had no other son, they did have three daughters but sadly Lady Cook died soon after giving birth to the third. Then as the years passed and Walter approached his twentieth birthday his father remembered the words of the gipsy and he became very worried.

He decided to build a strange tower into which no one could enter except with the permission of a person locked inside. He then showed the scroll to his son and told him the story of the Romany man. He begged him to lock himself away in the tower for one year and not come out again until his twenty-first birthday had passed. But the youth laughed at the idea until he saw how serious his father was, so to please him he did as his father requested. He was made as comfortable as possible and given everything that he wanted. Luxuries and necessities were hauled up in a basket by ropes and every day Walter's father or sisters sat beneath the tower to converse with him.

As the months went by the father became more confident that all was going to be well. He had done his best to stave off disaster and he longed for the day of his son's release. The night before the young man's twenty-first birthday the father and daughters stood beneath the tower and asked Walter if he wanted anything. The son replied,

"As the night is chilly and I have little fuel, will you send me up a faggot. Thank God this is the last time I will have to dip and draw for my needs, it is always weary work to the arms."

When the faggot had been pulled up Walter said, "Now I will wish you good night my father and dear sisters. Just look at Mars, the star of my fate. See how he shines so brightly tonight. All will be well as we will see."

The father looked up but at that moment a dark cloud obscured the planet and made him shudder at the omen. He retired to bed but he couldn't sleep and went to his window to watch the flickering of the firelight shining from the tower. The sisters also had a restless night interrupted by troubled dreams. The next morning they went to stand beneath the tower and they called to Walter, but they got no reply.

"Quick, fetch a ladder," shouted Sir Maurice and a servant rushed to get the ladder and placed it against the tower wall. He climbed up and looked in at the window. He then called down,

"Young master's asleep – Fast asleep."

"Come down," shouted Sir Maurice. "Let me go up and take a look."

He quickly climbed the ladder and scrambled in through the open window. He went over to his son but he found that Walter was not sleeping, but dead. An adder was twisted around his arm and blood was on his neck. The snake had slithered from the faggot during the night and fulfilled the gipsy's prophecy.

The Legend of Avalon, Vincent and Goram

An ancient Bristol legend tells of two sibling giants named Vincent and Goram who lived on what we know today as Clifton Down. These brothers competed for the love of a beautiful maiden named Avalon who lived 3 leagues to the east on the high ground overlooking a great lake called Merdöll. She was a cousin of Freyja, the Goddess of love and beauty who dwelt in Asgard; the ancient abode of the Gods. But Avalon rivalled Freyja in beauty and was the fairest maiden ever to live on earth. She was kind and generous to her people and she always made certain that they never went hungry, and if they needed skins to make new clothes, she provided them with the very best stags and hinds.

Avalon's own clothes were gifts from the Goddess's that they made especially for her because she was so tall. In the winter she wore magnificent white furs combed out of the underbellies of the huge Asgardian snow-yaks and woven into long flowing gowns. In summer her attire was that of the finest Asgard gossamer in the purest silvery-white. During the warm summer months, when few clothes were needed, she bathed every day in the great lake near her home where the waters were cool and clear. Standing guard to make certain that no one could see her were two massive hounds named Garamond and Valliant. So beautiful was Avalon that even some of the Gods tried to win her love with flattery and wonderful gifts, but she was not a woman who was easily impressed and she always rejected their advances.

To try and win Avalon's affections, Vincent decided that he should do something so great that his name, and the name of Avalon, would be remembered forever. When he told his brother about his idea, Goram, not wanting to be left out of any grand scheme, said it would be better if they worked on a project together. He suggested that they should build a great tower of rocks mingled with the bones of the huge creatures that, in those ancient times at the end of the last ice age, inhabited the earth. Goram, being a lazy and gluttonous fellow, said that he would provide the bones from all the animals he ate, and Vincent could provide all the rocks.

This suggestion didn't meet with Vincent's approval and he said that to try and impress Avalon he was going to carve a gorge through the rocks at Rownham so as to drain the great lake, which stretched from the base of these rocks for twenty miles to the east. The waters would then flow to the sea creating a new river, which would help to drain the lands where herbs and crops could be grown and this would benefit people for many generations to come. He immediately set about his task and progressed so well that soon Goram, who had so far refused to help in this work, became worried that his name would be forgotten forever if he didn't do something equally as impressive.

To try and compete with his brother, Goram decided to hew out a rival gorge from the hills three miles to the north of Rownham. But he was too lazy to make his own pickaxe and so he arranged with his brother to share Vincent's axe. It was agreed that it should be thrown between them six times every day, but the first thing Goram did was to carve himself a great arm-chair in the rocks where he could sit and take it easy whenever he was not working. A shout of warning was to be given before the axe was sent on its way, but one afternoon Goram was fast asleep in his chair when Vincent shouted his warning and threw the axe. It hit Goram on the head and split his skull, killing him instantly. Vincent was so upset by what had happened that he worked even harder to finish his gorge. When the work was complete it created the new river, which Vincent named after the maiden that he and Goram had competed for, naming it the Avalon River. Vincent then left the area and wandered around looking for other tasks to perform to help take his mind of the terrible deed that he had done in killing his brother. He went north into the lands now known as Derbyshire where he carved the great Peak Cavern. He then strayed into the northern mountainous lands where he made the beautiful Staffa Cavern at the time when this island was still attached to the mainland. After this he worked his way across to the Emerald Isle building the Giant's Causeway as he went. Finally, tired and exhausted, he returned to his home and prepared to die, passing his final days seated upon the rocks of the gorge that he had created. Although he was never to know it, he did get his wish that his name should be remembered forever. The rocks of the gorge that he had created, and where he spent his final days, have been know by the name of Vincent's Rocks (now St Vincent's Rocks) ever since.

When Avalon saw what Vincent had done by carving out his gorge she was very angry. The new river had drained her beautiful lake and she no longer had her secluded bathing place to use in the summer months. But after a year had passed several of her people came to tell her how wonderful it was that they now had a great deal of new and fertile land to use for farming. Believing this to have been Avalon's idea they thanked her for this magnificent gift. So Avalon went down to walk along the riverbank and see for herself how much this new land had helped her people. As she was wandering towards the east she discovered three pools of clear warm water. These pools had been placed there as a gift from Sol, the Sun God, so that Avalon would still have a secret place in which to bathe. Because the waters were constantly warm she would now be able to bathe every day of the year. As Avalon began to think about this she could see how much better life was without the lake. She had a much better bathing place for herself, there was a lot more land for her people to use and the soil was more fertile than any other land for miles around. Soon vegetation began to grow and a lot of wildlife came into the area. Among this influx were hares and deer that could be hunted by the local people and used for meat and to provide skins for clothing.

Now Avalon started to believe that Vincent was right in what he had done and her annoyance with him slowly turned to admiration. She became so touched by his efforts to impress her that she set out to try and find him. Following the path that Vincent had taken to the north she became so impressed with the things he had created along the way that her admiration grew into love. But when she reached the Emerald Isle a family of dwarfs told her that Vincent was no longer there. They said he was very tired and weary and had become ill from all his strenuous labour. He had left the Isle to return to his homeland many months before, so Avalon made her way back to the West Country only to discover that she was too late and Vincent was already dead. In her sorrow she sat beneath the rocks of the gorge by the side of the river that Vincent had created and swallowed a poisonous herb. As the life drained away from her she fell forward into the river and her body sank to the bottom. Nereus, the God of rivers, took pity on her and immortalised Avalon by transforming her into the Goddess of the river that bore her name. In an old poem the maiden's name was incorrectly written as Avona, a name that was taken from Avon, a corruption of the word *afene*, the Celtic word for river. But just like Vincent, Avalon's name lives on as the Goddess of the Avon, the river that flows through the beautiful gorge created for her by the one who loved her so much.

The Story of Sabrina

In the middle years of the Roman occupation of Britain there lived a beautiful Romano-British princess named Sabrina. She lived with her parents in a luxurious villa on the western edge of Aquae Sulis near the banks of the Avalon River. When she was 18 years old she fell in love with Estrildis, the Celtic leader of one of the Dobuni tribes of ancient Briton who lived at Caer Brito, the fortified town that later became the City of Bristol. Sabrina was so much in love with Estrildis that she ran away from home to go and live with him. This angered her mother to such an extent that in a fit of rage she gathered her supporters together and attacked Estrildis and his army in a field to the north of Caer Brito. In the ensuing battle over 100 men were killed including Estrildis who died with a sword-blade to his heart.

When Sabrina was told of his fate she became so upset that she told her mother that she never wanted to see her again. She ran away to the northwest until she came to the turbulent waters of the River Sture. Not wanting to live without her true love, she removed her clothes and threw herself into the river and drowned in the swirling tide. However, the river god Nereus found her naked body drifting around in the undercurrent and took pity on her and transformed her into the goddess of the river that took her life. It then became known as the Sabrina River and the estuary that it flowed into, the Sabrina Sea. During the Saxon era the name of the river was changed to the River Severn and the estuary became known as the Severn Sea.

Tombstone of Mystery

In the graveyard of St Luke's Church in Brislington, Bristol there is a mysterious tombstone. It is dated 1542 and commemorates Thomas Newman who died that year at the age of 153. Beneath the name and age it says: *This Stone was new faced in the Year 1771 to Perpetuate the Great Age of the Deceased.* So who was Thomas Newman and did he really live to such an incredible age? As unlikely as it seems the mystery does not end there. In a churchyard in Bridlington, North Yorkshire there is a mysterious tombstone dated 1542 with the inscription: '*Thomas Newman aged 153 years. This stone was refaced in 1771 to preserve the recollection of this remarkable prolongation of human life.*' Beneath this it says: '*The above is a copy of an inscription on an ancient stone of Bridlington churchyard, which has now disappeared.* '

It would be incredible for *any* man to live for 153 years, but for two men to live for such an age must surely be impossible. Even more unlikely would be for them both to be named Thomas Newman, for them both to have been born in the same year of 1389, and for one to be buried in Brislington, Bristol and the other in Bridlington, Yorkshire. So is it that the stone in the Brislington churchyard is the original stone that disappeared from the Bridlington churchyard? This is unlikely because if it were then why is the wording on the Bristol tombstone slightly different from that quoted as having been on the original Yorkshire tombstone? There is also the question of why would a tombstone be removed from a churchyard in Bridlington and transported by cart or wagon almost 250 miles to a churchyard in Brislington where it is known to have been situated since long before the time that it was refaced?

But if there *were* originally two stones (located over 200 miles apart) then is it just a coincidence that they were both refaced at the same time in the year 1771, and in an age when communications were very poor? And is it really possible for there to have been two men named Thomas Newman, each having been born in 1389 and dying at the age of 153 in 1542, one in Brislington, Bristol and the other in Bridlington, Yorkshire? Or was there just one Thomas Newman who was buried in Bristol? If this were so then why did he have a tombstone in both Brislington and in Bridlington? And if there was originally only one tombstone, then why was it at some time taken to Bridlington only to be returned to Brislington a few years later? The wording on the Brislington tombstone suggests this is the *original* stone, which means it was never situated in Yorkshire, so why does the inscription in the Bridlington churchyard say that it was? This could only mean that there *were* two separate tombstones and the one in Bristol is still in its original place. So from this evidence it seems there really were two Thomas Newman's, but is that too incredible to be believed? This is a mystery that may never be solved.

The Veiled Lady

On a cold winter's night in December 1896 a young couple left their house in Mary-le-Port Street, Bristol on their way to visit a friend who lived near the western end of Nicholas Street. They crossed over High Street and into the dark and gloomy Nicholas Street, which was lighted by nothing more than a few flickering gas lamps. As they were passing the lower end of St Nicholas Market they saw the figure of a woman walking slowly towards them out of the gloom. By the woman's side was a young boy who momentarily glanced up at the woman and then returned his gaze to the young couple. A strange feeling suddenly came over the couple for there was something about the woman that made them stop in their tracks. An icy tingle ran down their spines as the woman and the boy came closer, but then they stopped about ten feet before reaching them. The couple saw that the woman was wearing an unusual hat, which seemed to have forward pointing projections at each side and at the front, something like the shape of a multiple holly leaf. From beneath the hat a veil hung down across the woman's face and over her left shoulder.

The woman stared at them through her veil for a moment and then she began to move slowly back, but seeming to float rather than walk. The boy turned his head and looked at her and then reached out his arms, but the woman continued to move away. The boy dropped his arms and watched as the woman began to rise in to the air. She rose about ten feet and then turned towards the building on the couple's right. She backed straight into it but as soon as she hit the wall her body disappeared as though it had passed right through leaving nothing but her veiled face staring down at the terrified young couple. She then looked down at the boy but as he stood in the street sobbing and reaching his hands up to the woman, he also began to move away. It seemed to the young couple that he was being dragged by his waist by an invisible force, back the way he had come. He was drifting backwards at an accelerating rate with his body leaning forwards at about 45° and his outstretched arms still reaching for the woman. He gave a sorrowful cry, which, like his physical form, quickly disappeared into the night. The head of the woman seemed to turn slightly to watch him go and then it remained motionless as if in a petrified state.

Trembling with fright at what they had seen, the couple felt as though they had been frozen to the spot but now, regaining the use of their legs they turned and ran as fast as they could, back along Nicholas Street. They didn't stop running until they reached the door of their house and rushing inside they slammed the door shut and bolted it. Huddled together on their old settee the young couple were unable to speak to each other for almost an hour. They put some more wood on the fire but when it was gone neither of them wanted to go out to the backyard to get some more. They just wrapped themselves in a blanket and waited for the sun to come up.

The following morning, in the light of day, everything seemed different and they began to doubt their senses. After eating their breakfast they decided to go and take another look at the façade of the building through the wall of which the woman had so mysteriously vanished. As they began to walk along Nicholas Street they saw a crowd of about a dozen people staring up at this vary same building. As they approached they could see what it was that the people were staring at. Across the façade were four sculptured heads representing the four seasons. They were well known to people in that area because they had been there since the building was erected in 1868. The first head was that of a boy with spring flowers in his hair. The second was that of a young woman, her hair entwined with summer fruits. The third head represented autumn and was a mature woman with harvest corn in her hair. The fourth was that of Old Father Winter; an old man with a beard and the hood of his cloak pulled over his head.

But now there was something different about them for one of the heads had changed. The third head, that of the woman representing autumn, now had a veil across her face that was pulled onto her left shoulder. Not a material veil that someone had placed there as a joke but a stone veil that was now a part of the sculpture itself. Also, the corn had disappeared and was replaced by a strange hat with forward facing points at each side. The veil hung down from beneath the hat but although it was made of stone, the face could still be seen quite clearly. No one could understand what had happened. Some people began to believe that the face had always been like that, but others said they had never seen the veil before.

But this was not the only strange thing about the four sculptured heads. Although summer and winter appeared to be exactly as they had always been, the first sculpture (that of a boy representing spring) was now missing from its niche. Nothing was left within the niche but a plain flat surface as if nothing had ever been there. But was it possible for someone to come along during the early evening of the night before and remove this head and replace that of autumn with a sculpture of a veiled lady? This is unlikely because it would have been too big and noisy a job, even for a team of men, especially as they would have been working by the light of nothing more than a few flickering gas lamps. People living in the nearby houses said that they didn't hear or see anything, especially people putting up scaffolding in order to do the work. So this was clearly not something that could have been done by any human hands.

The following year a craftsman was employed to make a replacement head for spring. He first made a latex mould of the head of summer and used this to make the new casting. This casting he altered the best he could by trying to change the summer fruits into spring flowers. He also altered the cloak slightly although this wasn't really necessary and he didn't do a very good job. However, this new head was fixed into its niche and even though it was better than no head at all, it still looked virtually the same as that of summer.

But it had taken three men two days to erect the scaffolding, fix the head in place and then remove the scaffolding from the site. This shows that the original head could not have been removed so cleanly, over one night and during the hours of darkness. And there would certainly not have been enough time during that same evening for any team of men to remove the head of autumn and replace it so expertly with the head of the Veiled Lady.

But this was not the end of the mystery because, as the months went by, other strange events concerning the face of the Veiled Lady began to happen. Some people reported looking at the sculpture and seeing the eyes suddenly open from behind the veil. This was always followed by misfortune to the person who had looked into the eyes. Sometimes it was just a minor misfortune and sometimes it was something very bad. Others reported seeing the woman smile at them and this was always followed by a stroke of good luck. These reports continued until the time of the First World War when most people's minds were diverted away from the Veiled Lady. Now the story of the young couple's vision was almost lost. Between the two Great Wars only a few people reported seeing the woman's smile or looking into her eyes; but since 1945 the stories of the Veiled Lady have completely faded away. In recent years the four sculptured heads have been painted and the effect of the lady's eyes and smile have gone. Although the sculpture still remains, perhaps the spirit of the Veiled Lady has finally been laid to rest. But who knows whether it has or not? Just go and take a look for yourself, and look deeply into her eyes. That is, *if you dare*!

The Blackness

At the request of her family, the lady in this story will simply be known as Mrs T.

In the early hours of the morning on 21st October 1966, an elderly lady named Mrs T of Clifton in Bristol suddenly woke from her sleep screaming and gasping for air. Her daughter rushed in to the old woman's bedroom to see what was wrong.

"I can't get out," cried the mother. "Help me, the black thing is all around. I can't move. I'm trapped. It has got me and I can't get away."

"It's alright mother," said the daughter, "I'm here with you. You're having a nightmare."

Slowly coming into consciousness, Mrs T was trembling with fear as she opened her eyes. "Oh my God, it was awful," she said. "I was a little girl again in my hometown of Merthyr Vale. I was deep in a coalmine and suddenly it collapsed on top of me. Then the coal began to move like a flowing river and I was carried along for mile after mile until it somehow burst out into the open air. I slid in the coal, down the side of a mountain as if I were in an avalanche. Down and down I went into a valley until I crashed through the side of a building. There were people in there but I couldn't see them because the coal had buried me again, trapping me solid so I couldn't move. I could only hear people screaming and shouting for help, and most of them seemed to be children. But then it was quiet and I struggled to get out but I couldn't move. It was awful and so real, I felt it was actually happening. But someone tried to pull me out but he couldn't manage it because the coal kept falling back on top of me. It seemed to be one of the children, a small boy with dark hair and a long fringe. Then he said he was sorry but there was nothing he could do. It all went black again and I was no longer able to move."

The evening before Mrs T's nightmare a group of people were attending a meeting at a Spiritualist Church in Plymouth. As they sat and meditated one of the women drifted away, almost into a dream-like sleep. While in this state she had a terrifying vision of what appeared to be a coal-mining disaster. She saw a vast avalanche of coal bursting out of a mountain and hurtling down into a valley where an old schoolhouse stood. When the dust had settled she saw, at the bottom of the mountain of coal, the figure of a small boy with dark hair and a long fringe, standing alone and looking forlorn. For many minutes she watched a rescue operation taking place as miners and local people tried in vain to dig out those trapped beneath the coal. But try as they did there was nothing they could do. The little boy was the only one who was saved and she saw him being led away by one of the rescuers – a man wearing an unusual peaked cap.

When the woman came out of her dream she told the other people present at the meeting about her vision but none of them had any idea what, if anything, it meant. At 8.30 the following morning she went to see one of her neighbours and told her the story but she also, had no idea what the vision could mean. Then, just forty-five minutes later, at 9.15 on the morning of the 21st October 1966, the woman's premonition, and the nightmare of old Mrs T came true. Across the Bristol Channel in South Wales, an avalanche of coal slid down a mountainside and engulfed a school in the mining town of Aberfan one mile to the north of Merthyr Vale. In just a few seconds 128 children and 16 adults were killed, crushed to death by the colossal mountain of coal. The disaster was described in one newspaper as 'the greatest single disaster that has ever hit our people in peace-time.' From this tragedy only one person survived. A small boy with dark hair and a long fringe was led away by one of the villagers, a man wearing an unusual peaked cap. The boy's face was blackened with coal-dust as tramlines of tears cut through the grime as they rolled down his cheeks. He had not been to school that day because he was feeling unwell but when he heard of the tragedy he went with his father to see if there was anything he could do to help; but of course there was nothing.

In Bristol, Mrs T and her daughter were listening to the lunchtime news on the radio when the Aberfan disaster was reported. The shock to the old woman was so great that the blackness came over her like a shroud and she collapsed, never to see the light of day again.

These were not the only reports of people foreseeing this disaster. Four days earlier a woman in Sidcup told two of her friends that she had a terrible dream. She said it was a vivid nightmare of a disaster in a coal-mining village. It was in a valley where there was a school full of children. She saw a mountain of coal and water rushing down into the valley burying the school, and the screams of the children were so vivid that she woke up screaming herself.

But saddest of all was on the morning of the disaster a little girl told her mother that she didn't want to go to school that day. The mother asked her why and the girl said that she had a dream about going to school but when she arrived it was no longer there. Something black had come down and covered it over. The mother wouldn't listen and sent her daughter to school as usual, but tragically this child was one of the victims who were killed in the Aberfan mine disaster that day.

Story written as a tribute to the 128 children and 16 adults who lost their lives.

Princess Caraboo

On the afternoon of Thursday, 3rd April 1817 a young woman was seen wandering around in the lanes of Almondsbury just to the north of Bristol. She was dressed in the garb of a foreign gipsy and was of Asiatic appearance, 5'2" tall and aged about 25. She seemed to be lost and extremely weary and very much in need of help; but when some of the villagers tried to find out who she was and where she had come from none of them could understand what she was saying because she spoke in an unusual foreign language. The local shoemaker thought perhaps she was hungry and he gave her some bread and butter, but that wasn't what she really wanted. As he was unable to help the woman he decided to take her to the home of the local vicar, the Rev Hunt. Unfortunately the reverend was not at home, but his wife was in the kitchen and she came out and tried to communicate with the gipsy, but she had little success until the woman made signs that she was tired and wanted to sleep there. However, Mrs Hunt refused this request because she didn't want a foreign gipsy staying in her house. Not really knowing what to do, the only thing she could think of was to send for Mr Overton, the Parish Poorhouse Overseer.

When Overton arrived he had no more idea of what to do than Mrs Hunt or any of the villagers. In need of guidance, he left the woman with Mrs Hunt and went immediately to Knole Park, the home of Samuel and Elizabeth Worrall and told them about the young foreign woman. As Mr Worrall was the Gloucestershire County Magistrate, Overton thought it best to seek his advice about what to do. Also, one of Worrall's male servants was able to converse in several foreign languages so it was thought that he might be able to communicate with the woman. From the description of her, Mrs Worrall had a feeling that she might be something other than just a gipsy so she suggested that as the evening was approaching the young woman should be taken to the Bowl Inn and given a bed for the night and then they could decide what to do about her the following morning. But Overton said that the woman seemed nervous and confused and would be unlikely to go with him, so Mrs Worrall asked two of her servant girls to go along as well and try to find out anything they could about this mysterious woman. Mr Worrall said that the following Saturday the woman should be taken before the City Fathers in Bristol because he thought that she was probably nothing more than a vagrant. Mrs Worrall, on the other hand, felt this was wrong and said that if this is what was to be done then she would attend the hearing herself and ask her friend Jane Worsthorn to go with her so that they could judge the young women for themselves and, if she really were something other than a gipsy or a vagrant, work out a way to help her.

Overton returned to Mrs Hunt to inform her of what had been decided. As he and the servant girls led the gipsy from the Rev Hunt's house she was so weary and exhausted that she had to be helped to walk along the road. At one point she almost collapsed and had to lean on Overton's arm for support. When they reached the Bowl Inn the landlady was asked, on behalf of Mrs Worrall, to give the woman a comfortable bed in a private room and to make certain that she had a good supper. Overton and the two servant girls then left the Bowl and returned to their homes.

The following morning (which was a Good Friday) Mrs Worrall rose very early and went to the Bowl before attending church to take some essential items for the young woman's use. When Mrs Worrall arrived she was shown into the parlour by the landlady Mrs Pratt who said, with great excitement, how the woman had refused to sleep in the bed and pointed to the floor as if she didn't understand what a bed was for. Mrs Pratt was unable to make her comfortable until her little girl Emily climbed in to the bed and made the woman understand what she should do. When supper was brought she would only eat the bread and nothing else and she prayed over it before breaking off small pieces to eat. She was very well mannered and clean and insisted on her cup being washed after every use. She also repeated a prayer before and after drinking and she knelt in prayer for a considerable time before eventually getting in to the bed.

Mrs Worrall was then taken to the young woman's room but as she entered she saw the woman weeping silently by the bedside. When the woman looked up she immediately rose to her feet and rushed over to Mrs Worrall with a look of pleasure as if recognising that she was a kind-hearted woman of great standing in the community. She threw herself at Mrs Worrall's feet and bowed her head so low that it touched the floor. She then began to salaam and kiss the hem of Mrs Worrall's dress. The Rev Hunt, who had been told of this foreigner by his wife, arrived at the Bowl (accompanied by Overton) with many books and maps, thinking that the woman might recognise pictures of her own country. When she started to look at them she immediately pointed to a map of China and made them understand that she knew this country, although it was obvious that she was not Chinese herself. But wherever she was from she was certainly very intelligent and quick to understand things. Mrs Worrall then tried to persuade her to accompany her and Overton back to Knole Park – but the woman seemed reluctant to do that. She obviously didn't know where she was to be taken but Mrs Worrall managed to assure her, with friendly gestures, that all was going to be well.

Just after leaving the Bowl, they were passing the churchyard gate when the woman suddenly ran through the gate and up to the church door. Finding it to be locked, she seemed to be disappointed and slowly walked back to Mrs Worrall and Overton. What her intention had been in doing this neither Mrs Worrall nor Overton had any idea but she could have been looking for sanctuary. When they arrived at Knole Park, Mrs Worrall invited Overton and the woman inside but the woman now became very agitated and was reluctant to enter, appearing to be terrified of something. She was only persuaded to go inside after a lot of coaxing by Mrs Worrall. Once inside, Samuel Worrall joined them and together they tried to communicate with the woman but neither Mr or Mrs Worrall, nor the servant, were able to understand anything the young woman said. They looked for clues as to her origins but in her possessions all she had was a bag of personal items such as a few English coins, a comb and a small bar of soap wrapped in a piece of linen. Then the woman noticed that some of the servants were eating hot cross buns for their breakfast. She immediately took one of these but instead of eating it, she broke off the cross and placed it on her dress like a crucifix. So it seemed from this that she was probably a Christian, which could have been the reason why she tried to run into the church.

Mr and Mrs Worrall agreed to look after the woman until the next morning, although Mr Worrall still treated her with a great deal of suspicion. However, they were both intrigued to know more about her and the following morning Mrs Worrall tried once again to communicate with her but, unable to understand the language, she suddenly had an idea. She wrote her name on a piece of paper and spoke the name while pointing to herself. She then gave the pen to the woman and asked her to do the same but she seemed unable to write, or at least to write in English, and she refused to take the pen. But then, as if understanding what Mrs Worrall had been asking, the woman cried out "Caraboo" and pointed to herself. Mrs Worrall thought this to be such a strange and beautiful name that she believed the woman could be someone very special. Using a globe of the world she tried to see if the woman could indicate exactly where she came from. After looking at the globe for a while the young woman pointed to a place near Sumatra in the East Indies and called out the name "Javasu."

"So her name is Caraboo and she comes from Javasu," thought Mrs Worrall, but despite her intrigue she was unable to prevent Caraboo from being taken to court in Bristol that morning to be charged with vagrancy. Mr Worrall insisted on this because he still didn't trust the young woman and thought she should be properly tried. He sat next to the mayor in the courtroom but as the trial progressed he began to think that perhaps he had been wrong in bringing this woman before the City Fathers. They in their turn decided that the woman *was* a vagrant and should be punished according to the law. This meant there was nothing Mr Worrall could do to prevent the charge from being enforced and Caraboo was committed to Bristol's Workhouse of St Peter's Hospital. She was to be placed there until something transpired about who she really was and where she had come from. But even in the workhouse her manner was peculiar, almost as if she had the expectation of being obeyed, making it seem as though she must be a person of some rank in her own country. Even her posture was always very erect and highly distinctive.

After three days Mrs Worrall managed to get Caraboo released into her custody and she took her back to her home at Knole Park. The news of this intriguing foreign woman soon got around and over the following weeks many prominent people came to visit the young woman, including a Marquis who brought with him a Portuguese gentleman named Manuel Eynesso. The Marquis hoped that Eynesso would be able to understand Caraboo's language because he had spent many years in the Far East. During the visit Caraboo acted in a perfect manner and in such a way as to appear of higher rank than the Marquis himself. Eynesso spoke with Caraboo for a while and then informed the Worrall's that he understood her language well. He said it was a dialect from the islands in the East but it was not pure, which is why it had been so difficult to understand. He said she seemed to be a princess from Sumatra and was abducted by pirates and brought to England. Mrs Worrall said that she had guessed that Caraboo was not an impostor (as some people had thought) and that she really was a person of great importance.

As the weeks went by Mrs Worrall continued to communicate with the princess, even learning many of the words of her language. She discovered that the princess had been taken prisoner by raiding Chinese pirates that she called the *Tap Abu*. On the voyage to the west she was ill treated, but as they were sailing up the Severn (the reason for which isn't known) she escaped and jumped overboard and swam to the shore. But from the moment she arrived at the Worrall's home she began to perform some very strange rituals. Every morning she went up on to the roof and began singing strange songs and chants that were believed to be prayers. She also entertained the Worrall's and their guests with wonderful dances. She was so enchanting that 70-year-old Rev Tucker, who had come from Bath to see the princess, tried to flirt with her but he was immediately stopped and put in his place by Mrs Worrall.

On the afternoon of 23rd April, Mr and Mrs Worrall were walking in the sunshine with Caraboo and two of their friends, Amelia and Elizabeth Brooking, when Caraboo suddenly surprised everyone when she ran up a bank, threw her arms in the air and dived fully clothed into the lake. She disappeared from view for several seconds but when she reappeared she swam with great strength to the island in the middle of the lake. When she was on dry land she turned and waved then ran into the trees. A few minutes later she reappeared and swam back to her waiting friends. When she emerged from the water her wet dress clung to her body in such a way that it looked as though she were almost naked. Mr Worrall gazed at her with great delight but Caraboo quickly ran back to the house, attempting to hide as much as she could from the prying eyes of the gardeners by dodging between the trees. Amelia Brooking was disgusted and said her behaviour was shocking and savage, but Mr Worrall pointed out that bathing was a healthy pursuit and that Caraboo was, after all, fully clothed.

Mr Worrall's valet, a man named Peterson, was instructed to row Caraboo out to the island in future so that she didn't have to swim there. Caraboo made herself a temple dedicated to her god *Allah Tallah* on the island, which was about two feet high, cross hatched with twigs and covered in wild flowers and laurel leaves. Here she worshiped twice every day, walking three times around the temple then kneeling to pray, covering her head with a shawl. Mr Worrall often rowed his wife out to the island so that they could watch this intriguing ritual together. But Mrs Worrall didn't really like Peterson rowing Caraboo out to the island because she thought he was a swarthy, greasy young man whom she had never trusted. Her dislike of him grew even stronger one day when he claimed that Caraboo was a fake and that she could understand and speak English very well. He said that when he was rowing Caraboo out to the island she wanted to do the rowing herself but he told her that she couldn't because she was carrying three pigeons to sacrifice to *Allah Tallah*. He stopped in the middle of the lake and told Caraboo that she is a cheat. Peterson said she immediately replied, "Caraboo no cheat." When Peterson said, "There you are, you do understand English," Caraboo stood up and tried to rock the boat to tip him out. However, Mrs Worrall said that Caraboo had learnt a few words of English and was beginning to understand, so she wouldn't listen to Peterson and refused to believe that Caraboo was an impostor.

As the days passed, Caraboo's habits became even stranger, especially her eating habits. Her diet was mainly of rice and to drink she would only have water or tea. She insisted on preparing all her food herself and always made it very savoury, being very fond of Indian curry. When eating meat she would always sacrifice it, taking a pigeon, rabbit or fish and beheading it then burying the head in the earth. She would then kneel in prayer to *Allah Tallah* facing the spot where the head was buried. She then collected wood to make a fire before wrapping the headless carcase in mud and roasting it in the hottest part of the fire. Sometimes she held little parties around the fire and she always prayed before and after eating her meals. After dining she always washed her hands and face in the lake. Every Tuesday she took her meal on to the roof of the tower to eat it, even though the climb was very dangerous.

The news of Caraboo spread far and wide and it wasn't long before many more prominent visitors began to turn up at the Worrall's house to meet her. A cavalcade of carriages came up the drive each day and the villagers were all agog as they lined the street to watch. Most of the visitors brought Caraboo a gift in the hope that it was something from her land, or something that reminded her of home. Caraboo was enchanted with all the fuss and attention being paid to her and as a thank you she sometimes danced for the visitors.

One day a Captain Palmer called bringing with him many books and maps and with these he sat to discuss their contents with Caraboo and Mrs Worrall. From their conversation and gestures it was discovered that the name of the captain of the pirate ship whose men had captured her was Chee Min. The ship was single-masted and had no guns, and her colours were, unusually, the Venetian war colours. A pirate named Tappa Boo commanded a second vessel (a brig with forty men) and this ship flew the Spanish national colours. As they continued to talk to Caraboo, Mrs Worrall and Captain Palmer began to learn many words and sentences of Caraboo's language. They discovered that her father's country was called "*Congee*," which Palmer thought to be China. Her mother was from "*Maudins*" meaning Malays, and her teeth were blackened, possibly from chewing Beatle Nuts. Her father, whose name was Jessee Mandu, had three other wives and Caraboo's name was once Sissu Mandu, which was later changed to Caraboo. They also learnt that *macratoos* were common men and *boogoos* were black cannibals.

The purpose of Caraboo's abduction was not clear but it may have been slavery. Using signs and with the use of the books Caraboo was able to indicate to Palmer that she was a princess and that she had been walking in her garden with her three *sammen* (female servants) when Chee Min and his men captured her and carried her off. Caraboo's father managed to kill one of the men with an arrow and Caraboo wounded two others with her *crease* or dagger, one of which died. But the pirates escaped with Caraboo and took her aboard their ship. Eleven days later Caraboo was sold to Tappa Boo and transferred to his vessel. After four weeks of sailing, the brig anchored at a port named *Batavia* and remained there for two days. It was at this port that another four women were brought aboard, although Caraboo was unable to understand their language so she didn't know where they were from. Caraboo's hair, which had been very long, was now cut short, as was that of the other women. After five more weeks of sailing they anchored at a port off the Cape of Good Hope where the four other women were taken ashore. They remained at this port for three days and then sailed for Europe, which they reached after eleven weeks of sailing. It was off the coast of the Bristol Channel, just north of the mouth of the Avon, that Caraboo jumped overboard and swam ashore.

Within five weeks of her arrival in Almondsbury, Caraboo could understand many English words and Mrs Worrall was able to understand many words of Javasu. Caraboo always entertained the Worrall's with her antics and her strange ways and they became very fond of her. Then one day, on 12th May, the Worrall's had to go to the funeral of their friend Jabez Carter and asked Caraboo to go with them, but she was afraid and refused to go. So the Worrall's went without her but when they returned from the church with several of their friends they found that Caraboo was nowhere to be seen. Mrs Worrall and her friend Jane Worsthorn searched everywhere they could think of. Mr Worrall got the servants to search the house and the grounds and eventually there came a shout from Joseph the gardener, "She is found." He had spotted Caraboo in the cedar tree right up in the uppermost fork. They pleaded with her to come down but she was reluctant to do so and seemed afraid of something, but eventually she agreed. She seemed very frightened – but of what? Tears filled her eyes at having caused such anxiety but would not say why she had climbed the tree. Then the Worrall's friend Mrs Pike spoke softly to Caraboo and gently drew the explanation out of her. It seems she was frightened of being alone in the house and had climbed the tree to escape contamination from men.

The following Sunday morning Caraboo appeared at breakfast in full war attire that she had made for herself. She gestured that it was her father's forty-seventh birthday and she wanted to honour him. She had tied a dinner gong to her back, the sound of which brought the servants running. Caraboo was fully dressed for war and hanging from her belt on one side she had a sword that she had made from a stick. Over her left shoulder was a bow and a quiver full of arrows. Her headdress was made of flowers and feathers placed within a few twisted branches of laurel. Her face was painted in stripes with charcoal. "Me war," she said smiling happily. Mrs Worrall then told Caraboo that she and her husband were going to church soon but this time they would leave a servant girl there to keep her company. But Caraboo said, "Me come," and excitedly danced around. Of course, Mrs Worrall said that she couldn't go to church looking like that but Caraboo replied, "Father's birthday." Mrs Worrall tried to explain that the congregation would look at her instead of listening to the Rev Hunt's sermon, so she had to stay there.

As the Worrall party, which included most of their servants, started walking down the hill, Caraboo came running after them, her gong clattering on her back. "She's surely not going like that," said Mr Worrall sounding very cross. "But it's her father's birthday so how can we refuse," said his wife. On entering the church it caused a sensation. The Rev Hunt bowed to the Worrall's as they walked through the doorway but when he saw Caraboo he suddenly froze and his mouth dropped open. As Caraboo walked up the

34

isle several villagers stood on their pews to get a better look. When Caraboo was in the box she was no longer visible but the congregation still caught an occasional glimpse of her feathers waving about. In his sermon the Rev Hunt said, "We must remember, we are all God's children and although some of us behave in a pagan manner, there is still a Christian heart beating within." The Worrall's were well acquainted with all the tenants and the farmers in Almondsbury so this incident was a great embarrassment to them. Amelia and Elizabeth Brooking, two of the village gossips, didn't even wish the Worrall's good morning as they left the church. Instead they rushed home as fast as they could to spread the news of Caraboo's appearance in church.

On 17th May the Bristol artist Edward Bird approached Mrs Worrall and offered to paint a portrait of Caraboo free of charge. Mrs Worrall thought this was a wonderful idea but offered to pay fifty guineas for the picture. However, Bird refused because he said that to paint a portrait of Caraboo would increase his reputation. When Mrs Worrall explained to Caraboo that the artist had suggested a visit to his studio that very afternoon, Caraboo was so excited that she immediately rushed to dress herself in her finest clothes.

Within a few hour news that Caraboo was coming to Bristol for her portrait to be painted had somehow got around. A large crowd had gathered along the streets to see her and as she drove past in the carriage with Mrs Worrall a voice shouted, "Three cheers for the Princess Caraboo." When she heard this and saw the people's reactions she waved and salaamed the crowd whereupon a great cheer went up. This made Mrs Worrall feel extremely proud. When they were in the studio, Bird said that he had assembled several important Patrons of the Arts of Bristol, which he wished to introduce to Caraboo.

The visit to Edward Bird's studio went well and the portrait of Caraboo was started. After Mrs Worrall and Caraboo returned to Knole Park they found that a letter had arrived from a Dr Wilkinson of Bath requesting a visit to see them. He said he might be able to discover the truth about Caraboo's identity and her country of origin, so Mrs Worrall agreed to his request. Wilkinson arrived at Knole on 22nd May and asked to see Mrs Worrall and Caraboo alone, stipulating that no other visitor should be present when he interviewed the princess. Caraboo was happy about this because she found Wilkinson to be very warm and friendly; she even danced for him and made a fuss of him. After the interview, Wilkinson said he was going to write to the *Bath Chronicle* about Caraboo and asked if he would be permitted to take her to India House to see the director. He also wrote letters to Oxford University's Mr Coplestone and to a Rev Whalley, both of who knew a great deal about the Far East. With these letters he included samples of Caraboo's writing and some of her drawings of her travels.

After Wilkinson had left, Caraboo seemed to be rather upset about his visit but Mrs Worrall couldn't understand why after she had treated him in such a friendly manner when he was there. Whatever the trouble was, Caraboo didn't say but the following day she disappeared from the house. The Worrall's and their servants searched the house and the grounds but unlike the last time she had disappeared, this time she was not to be found anywhere. But Caraboo returned in the evening two days later, covered in mud, badly blistered and so tired that she could hardly stand. She indicated that she had been to dig up her clothes, which she had hidden in a field to keep them from being found by the *macratoos*. But these clothes were not of a style you would expect from a country such as Javasu, they were a printed gown, a cotton bonnet and a shawl of typical English design. However, Mrs Worrall didn't question Caraboo about this because the poor young woman was suffering badly from a fever. She was taken to bed where she remained for several days until she had recovered.

In the mean time, on 1st June, Wilkinson had a description of Caraboo placed in the *Bath Chronicle* with the hope that someone might know who she is. As he and Mrs Worrall waited to see if there would be a response, Caraboo recovered from her fever and, on 6th June she disappeared again. As before, there was no sign of her anywhere but two days later a message was sent from Dr Wilkinson to Mrs Worrall to tell her that Caraboo had turned up in Bath. How she got there Mrs Worrall had no idea. When she received the message she left immediately and travelled alone to Bath where Wilkinson met her and took her to the house where Caraboo was being cared for. It was a large stone mansion set back from the street and as Mrs Worrall entered the building she passed a line of women waiting patiently upon the steps. Mrs Worrall didn't know who they were or what they were doing there. She just walked passed them and into the drawing room where she saw, to her amazement, Caraboo seated upon what looked like a throne, which was in fact an armchair with a red velvet cloak placed over it. A line of ladies stood before her waiting to be introduced and this was the reason for the queue. Caraboo seemed totally at ease, with two ladies kneeling at her feet. One held her hand and whispered to her while the other begged for a kiss. A third was behind her about to place a string of pearls around Caraboo's neck.

The princess looked up and as soon as she saw Mrs Worrall she seemed so delighted that she fell to her knees and salaamed, almost bringing Mrs Worrall to tears with emotion. She stood up and embraced Mrs Worrall with such passion that tears came into the eyes of almost all the ladies who were present. Caraboo's expression of joy at seeing her again was so overwhelming that Mrs Worrall began to doubt her senses. Why had Caraboo left if she cared so much for her? Then Caraboo suddenly dashed from the room as many of the ladies turned to each other asking where she had gone. Mrs Worrall ran after her and found her in the parlour. Caraboo made signs that she wanted to see Mrs Worrall alone to make her understand why she had left Knole Park. Using gestures and what little English she knew, she said that she was anxious to try and return to her family in Javasu. Mrs Worrall said there was no need for her to run away because if that was what she wanted, then she would do everything she could to help. When she spoke to Wilkinson about this, he said that one gentleman who had met Caraboo was so taken by her plight that he donated £500 to start a fund to send her home. Wilkinson then told Mrs Worrall how Caraboo had managed to get to Bath.

After leaving Knole Park she began to walk along the highway when she was picked up by a caravan driver and taken to the Packhorse Inn on the outskirts of the city. There she was looked after by the landlady and given a hot meal. The landlady's friend, Mr Carpenter, recognised Caraboo from her description in the newspaper and he sent word to Dr Wilkinson telling him that the princess was at the inn. Wilkinson arranged for Caraboo to be taken to his friend's house in Russell Street where people could come and see her, and then he sent a messenger to Mrs Worrall telling her where Caraboo was staying. Mrs Worrall thanked Wilkinson for all he had done then she and Caraboo left the house and returned to Knole Park. As they drove up the driveway, Caraboo was so overjoyed at being back that she called out "home," the first time she had ever used this word.

The following day Wilkinson had his letter reprinted in the *Bath Chronicle* in the hope that this time someone might read it who knew more about who Caraboo was and exactly where she had come from. His hopes were realised when a Bristol landlady named Mrs Neale read Dr Wilkinson's letter and immediately recognised the description. She went to see a gentleman of Clifton whom she was acquainted with by the name of Mr Mortimer and told him that she believed she knew who Caraboo was. Mortimer, who was a friend of the Worrall's, listened to what Mrs Neale had to say with great interest. Her story was that Caraboo was an impostor who was really a cobbler's daughter from Devonshire. She was a servant girl and her real name was Mary Baker. She had come to Bristol looking for work and had lodged with Mrs Neale, but unable to find any work she decided to sail for America. Unfortunately she didn't have the fare of £5 and so she made up her mind to beg for it in the guise of a foreigner. By the time she had saved enough money she went to Bristol Quay with the hope of travelling to Philadelphia but the ship had already sailed. So Mary Baker dressed up one morning in odd clothes and set off to make her fortune, leaving her trunk behind with the intention of sending for it later.

Mortimer was convinced by Mrs Neale's story and he decided he should go and see Mrs Worrall and break the news to her as gently as he could. When he arrived at Knole Park he was accompanied by the son of a wheelwright, a man who said he had met a girl whom he thought to be Spanish but answering Caraboo's description. That was on 17th March, two weeks before she entered Almondsbury. Mortimer and the wheelwright spoke with Mrs Worrall alone and although very shocked by this news, Mrs Worrall thought that perhaps she would now find out the truth about Princess Caraboo. Mortimer thought that Caraboo would lie and try to run away when faced with the truth and so they had to make a plan to deceive her. It was decided that

Mrs Worrall should take Caraboo to Mortimer's home in Bristol where she could be confronted by Mrs Neale. The next morning Mrs Worrall told Caraboo to dress in all her finery for she was taking her to Edward Bird to have her portrait completed. Unaware of the deception, Caraboo excitedly rushed to dress in her turban with blue feathers, jewelled clasp and woollen dress with gold embroidery.

She was very happy and smiling as they drove along the road to Bristol. When they stopped outside Mortimer's house Caraboo looked worried as if she guessed she had been found out. When Mrs Worrall said there was a surprise for her inside, Caraboo looked relieved and pleased. A crowd had gathered and applauded Caraboo as she stepped down from the carriage. Mortimer's housekeeper showed them into the kitchen where Caraboo and the housekeeper looked at books of China while Mrs Worrall went to the parlour to talk to Mrs Neale. After she had told her story, Mrs Neale left the room to wait in the adjoining chamber. Mrs Worrall then called for Caraboo to come and join her in the parlour. When she was seated Mrs Worrall confronted her with her true identity.

Caraboo first made out that she didn't understand and she fell on her knees and kissed the hem of Mrs Worrall's dress. Mrs Worrall now became quite stern and said, "Mary, get up, enough of this playacting. I know you are an impostor and a liar, and I have Mrs Neale your landlady here to prove it." With these words, Mary burst into tears and begged not to be sent back to her father. "It was only out of respect and love for you that I continued the deception," she said. "I soon found it impossible to stop even though I wanted to. I never willingly cheated you in any way. I had never meant to harm anyone but I have suffered so much over these past years that I wanted to do something to try and better myself." Mrs Worrall promised Mary that she would not send for her father, but only under certain conditions. First she must tell her full history from the moment she was born and second, she must tell her real name, her parent's names, and exactly where they lived. So Mary began with a story of living for four months in Bombay and then on the Isle of France as a nurse to a European family. But that was as far as she got because Mortimer, who had returned to the room, soon proved this story to be false. He ordered Mary to be seated at the desk and made her write in full, the past history of her life, saying that neither he nor Mary would leave the house until it was finished. As this would take several days, Mrs Worrall left the house and returned to her home at Knole Park to break the news to her husband.

The Story of Mary Wilcox

This story is adapted from the diary of events of Mary's early life that she wrote under the order of Mr Mortimer of Clifton. It therefore reads as a list of events rather than that of a story.

Mary, the daughter of Thomas and Mary Wilcox, was born in 1792, the second of eleven children, seven of which died in infancy. Her father was a cobbler in Witheridge, Devonshire who made a good living at his work, but after the Poor Law was introduced he fell on hard times when he lost many of his customers. As a child, Mary helped in the fields, walking around with a clapper to scare the crows from the corn but when she was eight years old she was sent out to work spinning wool. Like most country people she had to be tough to survive and she soon grew to become a tomboy and learnt how to swim and kill blackbirds with her bow and arrows. At the age of sixteen she fell ill with rheumatic fever and she only recovered after a long illness. She was then sent to work at the farm of a Mr Moon as a maid-of-all-works and to help look after his children. Mary was glad to get away from home because her father regularly beat her, and this was often without cause. After working for the Moon's for two years Mary asked for a raise. She asked Mrs Moon if she could have a 1/- a week instead of 10d but Mrs Moon became very anger about this and accused Mary of being greedy and ungrateful. She told her to go and pack her belongings and leave the house without delay.

Mary's father was also angry with her and treated her very badly but a few days later she left home and walked to Exeter looking for work. Here she was employed by Mr and Mrs Brooke at £8 a year to wash, iron and cook, and to make up the fires. But Mary was not happy with this job and after two months she left and was paid £2 for the work she had done so far; the most money she ever had. Feeling happy with her new wealth she went to the market and bought some new clothes. She purchased a white muslin dress, a bonnet and some slippers. Eager to try them on, she ran from the marketplace and hid behind a hedge to change. Happy and smiling she went home to show her family but once again her father was angry with her and called her a thief, accusing her of stealing the clothes. Her mother told her not to wear them because they were of a style that were only meant for ladies and not for the likes of her. She called her a harlot and twice hit her as hard as she could as a punishment. After that no one at home would speak to her and so, six days later Mary walked out. She left her new clothes behind and because she didn't have any money she went begging at houses. Some people gave her money but others called her a vagabond and horsewhipped her, because that is what they did to people of her sort. Because of this treatment she descended into such a state that one night she thought about killing herself. She went down a lane and tied her apron strings together intending to hang herself, but then a voice inside her told her that would be a sin. As she sat by a hedge an old man saw her crying and taking pity on her, he gave her 5/-. With this money she walked to Taunton where she stayed at the Three Queens lodging house for 2½d a night. There she stayed for three nights and after leaving the lodging house she headed for Bristol, seventy-five miles away. Now, with all her money gone, she once again begged for food and slept in haystacks along the way.

When she arrived in Bristol she continued to ask people for food but one kind gentleman sent her to see a Mr Freeman of the Strangers' Friendly Society, who lived by the drawbridge. Mr Freeman gave her 4/- for food and lodgings and sent her on her way. The next morning Mary set out for London but thieves set upon her and stole her 4/- just after she left Bristol. When she reached Calne in Wiltshire she knocked on the door of a house and asked a servant girl for food, but she was quietly told to go away. But then a man came to the door to see who was there and he invited her inside. Mary didn't trust him and was going to leave but the man insisted that she should enter. He grabbed her by the arm and took her into a dark gloomy room where he began to question her about whom she was and where she had come from. Mary refused to answer but the man said that he was a magistrate and he was going to send her back to her home. He asked her what her surname was but Mary didn't want to tell him. Then seeing a loaf of bread on the table, this gave her an idea and she said that her surname was Baker. Ordering Mary to remain where she was the man left the room and locked the door behind him. Terrified of staying there any longer, Mary seized this opportunity to escape and she climbed out through a window and ran away as fast as she could.

Continuing on her journey she became very tired and weary and thirty miles from London she became ill and fainted from hunger. A waggoner, who had two lady passengers with him, picked her up and offered to take her to London free of charge. At Hyde Park Corner the waggoner told Mary to get down because he could take her no further but the women were concerned and asked where she wanted to go. Mary said she had nowhere at the moment and so, supporting her on either side, the two women took her to St George's Hospital where they sat her on the step. The doors were locked and no one answered so, not knowing what else to do, they left her there to fend for herself. About a quarter of an hour later the watchman found her sitting on the step and he asked her whom she was but Mary could no longer talk because of her illness and fatigue, so the watchman took her to the nearby watch-house. He then fetched Mr Burgess, the hospital physician who said that Mary was in a very poor and dangerous condition. He took her to the hall and sat her in front of the fire to try and warm her up a bit. Mary was then put to bed in the hospital where she remained for a month. Her head was shaved and blistered to ease the fever and her back cupped at the same time. This treatment was very painful and made Mary cry in agony. After another month she was taken from the Fever Ward to the Decline Ward where she stayed until she had the strength to leave the hospital.

Mary was now taken to stay with a Mrs Matthews at No.1 Clapham Road Place. This woman was a demanding mistress who employed Mary to look after a Rev Puttenden, a clergyman who was the only man allowed in the house. This was not a happy situation and Mary soon pined for her freedom. She was not allowed to go out alone or to encourage any men. Meals were the only pleasure to be had for they always ate very well. But Mrs Matthews soon found Mary to be a good and intelligent servant and so she decided to try and improve her mind. Mrs Matthews's daughter Betsey (when she came home from school each day) taught Mary the alphabet and how to read and write. This is something that Mary learnt extremely quickly because she was very bright and intelligent. Then one day the Rev Puttenden asked Mary to tell him all about her parents and then he wrote to them to say that Mary was well and living in London. He and Betsey helped Mary to write her own letter to her parents, which the local vicar of Witheridge, the Rev Dickins, read to them. In this letter Mary signed herself as Mary Wilcocks.

As the years passed Mary became restless because she felt like a prisoner in this house. She longed to be free and to feel the sunshine and hear the birds sing. Then one day (after she had been there for three years) she was in the back yard hanging out the washing when she heard a young woman singing in the yard next door. She couldn't see the woman because of the high wall that separated the yards so she climbed on an upturned washing tub and looked over. The young woman was the cook and servant to the Jewish family who lived there. Her name was Abigail and it wasn't long before she and Mary became good friends. But Abigail was worried about Mary's appearance. She was very pale because she wasn't allowed to go out very much. So Abigail invited Mary to the wedding of her employer's daughter but Mrs Matthews wouldn't allow her to go. But not wanting to be stuck in the house any longer, they made a plan that Mrs Matthews would not be likely to object to. Mary said that she and Abigail had been invited to the Christening of the baby of a Mrs Baynes, who was an acquaintance of Mrs Matthews. Although Mrs Matthews thought it strange that Mary should be invited and not her, she still permitted Mary to go. But it wasn't long before the truth was discovered and Mary was severely scolded for her deceit. An argument took place and Mary, having had enough of living like a prisoner, decided to leave.

Once again she was out on the streets with nowhere to go but she soon found lodgings for eight days with a widow woman named Mrs Henry, who supplied Mrs Matthews with petticoats. This was on the outskirts of the city where wooden houses were rotting and falling down. Her lodgings were small and smelly and she didn't want to stay there any longer than she had to. She tried to find work but she was unable to get any in this very poor area. She asked widow Henry to send her trunk to her father together with a note telling her parents that she had left Mrs Matthews service and to say that she had now left England with a travelling family. She thought this would be the best thing to tell them because she didn't want her parents to know what terrible conditions she was now living in. Her father would have been furious with her if he had known the truth, that she had come to this state by her own doing.

Not knowing what she should do now, Mary decided to become a nun. That way she would be fed and looked after and although the life was hard, she would always have a safe home and be cared for. This idea had come to her when she saw the high walled building called the Magdalene in Blackfriars Road. Widow Henry told her she shouldn't go into a place like that but Mary said that her mind was made up and she would be going there right away. When she entered the building she was taken before a committee who questioned her about her past and asked her if she really wanted to stay there. She said that she did and so she was accepted and given a piece of paper with ADMITTED written on it and then ordered into the next room. From there she was taken to a bathroom and had all her clothes stripped from her. She was scrubbed clean and inspected for head lice and her hair was cut short and dusted to prevent insect infestation. She was dressed in the Magdalene dress of blue with white tippet and apron and a plain-bordered cap.

Now she thought her troubles would be over and she would be taken care of for the rest of her life. However, she soon began to think how strange it was that all the women in the nunnery were young and that some of them were girls aged between about six and twelve years. Believing them to be novices she took little notice of this but she had only been there for six months when, one day, she overheard two of the girls talking about their previous occupations. In her innocents, Mary had not realised that all the inmates of this place were ex-prostitutes. She questioned them about it and was told that she must have known because that is what the name Magdalene refers to. She went immediately to see Mr Prince; the man who had been on the committee when she was admitted and told him that she had made a mistake and thought this place was a nunnery. Prince could hardly believe what he was hearing and he became very abusive towards Mary. He summoned the council and they said that she must have known what this place was. They all began to shout at her and said that for the past six months she had kept a place that could have been taken by a girl of the streets who really needed it. Her clothes were returned to her together with a £1 note that she had when she arrived and she was ordered to leave the premises and never to return.

Now out alone on the dangerous streets of London, Mary felt very vulnerable so she decided to disguise herself as a man so that she could walk about without being molested. At a pawnbroker's shop off Blackfriars Road she exchanger her clothes for those of a gentleman. The pawnbroker was very sympathetic towards Mary and gave her some advice on how to behave, but he was worried about Mary's voice. But because she looked so young as a man, Mary didn't thing that her high voice would come amiss. She thanked the pawnbroker and, not wanting to stay in London any longer, she decided to return to her home in Devonshire. She set off the following morning on the long road home, sleeping in ditches at night and walking by day. One night she stayed at a tavern, the Green Man at Hatton, where a friendly ostler let her sleep in the stable.

When she was walking across Salisbury Plain two men on horseback overtook her and stopped a few yards ahead. Both wore masks and one of them had a pistol that he pointed at Mary as he asked for money. She said that she didn't have any and was hoping that they would give some to her. This caused the highwaymen to laugh and, thinking that Mary was a man, asked if she wanted to join them to look after their horses. She accepted this offer because she thought the men might give her food and shelter for a while. They led her through a swamp, which had deformed trees all around. Soon they came to a small house on the heath, hidden by tall thorn hedges. After they had been there for about an hour four other men arrived. They began to ask her many questions about herself but none of them suspected that she was not a young man. The captain said that if she was going to join them she would need to be able to shoot a pistol, something that Mary had never done before. They took her outside and gave her a loaded gun but when she fired it the shot gave her a searing pain in her arm and the noise rang right through her. It made her scream, which unfortunately gave the game away that she was not a man but a woman. A quarrel then broke out among the men as to what they should do with her. Some wanted to kill her, accusing her of being a spy, but others disagreed. Mary said that she was only trying to get back home to her family in Devonshire so the captain decided that as that county was a long way away, he would let her go if she promised not to reveal their hideout. This she did so the captain gave her a guinea to help her on her way and he wished her a safe journey. Another of the men also took pity on her and gave her 5/- before the captain put her on the road to Exeter. She arrived at Witheridge still wearing her men's clothes, much to the amazement of her father and mother. As her trunk had arrived from London she was now able to dress as a woman once again.

A few weeks later Mary went to Crediton where she worked for three months with a tanner named Mr Pring, but she couldn't stand the smell so she gave her notice and left. She set off on her travels once more and walked to Lattiford and then to a little village named Spring, near Calne. Here she worked for several months for a Mrs Brownjohn, a farmer's wife. The winter was soon upon them and this turned out to be very severe and they were cut off by deep snow from early January until mid March. They ate nearly all their food during this time and fearing that they may starve, Mrs Brownjohn sent Mary out to try and reach Calne market. But she didn't get far because she was caught in a snow blizzard and, unable to see where she was going, she fell deep into a ditch and couldn't get out. Mr Brownjohn became very worried about her and went out to try and find her the following morning.

When he eventually found her she was close to death but after a few days in bed she slowly recovered. Following that terrible experience she couldn't bear to be in that part of the country any longer and she returned to Exeter where she spent three months working as a cook.

During the time she was in Exeter she made up her mind to return to London and she set off without writing to her parents to tell them that she was going. In London she found lodgings in Billingsgate with Mrs Hillier, a fishmonger of Darkhouse Lane. They sold fish in the market and wrapped it in paper they bought in bulk from the stationers. The old paper was sometimes lawyers' briefs; sometimes love letters and sometimes pages of novels. Mary loved to read these papers even though Mrs Hillier told her not to, but when Mary went to the stationers to collect them; she always put some down her bodice to read later. It was when she was there one day that she met a man named John Henry Beckerstedt. He was handsome and polite and had flashing brown eyes, and Mary very soon fell in love with him. He was also taken with her and he asked the stationer all about her. He sent her letters and flowers to her address at Mrs Hillier's and he told her that he was a sailor and had just been released from his ship. They went out together many times and Mary soon learnt that he was half English and half Malayan. One evening they went to the Haymarket Theatre to watch a play about Omar, the South Seas Islander who was brought to England and made famous. He was played by a very tall man with a blackened face and wearing fantastic coloured clothes and feathers in his hair. He spoke the oddest words that no one could understand and he used hand gestures that seemed to relate perfectly to the words. This play really fired Mary's imagination as she conjured up wonderful images of far distant lands.

After Mary had been going out with Beckerstedt for several weeks Mrs Hillier warned her not to be so foolish. She said this man was no good and was not to be trusted. But Beckerstedt asked Mary to marry him and ignoring Mrs Hillier's advice, Mary accepted his proposal. She and Beckerstedt were married by a Romish Priest in a church on Whitechapel Road the following day. Mary and her husband remained in London at his lodgings for one month after their marriage and then they went to Kingston near Lewes. After that they travelled to Brighton before going to Battle. This was the happiest time of Mary's life and her husband taught her many words of the Malayan language and drew signs for her to copy. But Beckerstedt was spending his money fast until it was nearly all gone. One day he gave Mary some money and told her to go back to London. He said that he was going to Dover and from there to Calais looking for work on one of the French ships. He promised to write and send for her as soon as he was able, but for some unknown reason he never did. Mary didn't know what happened to him. He could have been taken by a Press Gang or maybe he left because Mary was pregnant and he didn't want to be tied to any children.

Back in London, Mary found work with a Mrs Clark who ran the Crab Tree Inn on Tottenham Court Road where there was a large company of servants. Mr Clark was a gross and lecherous old man who molested many of the servant girls. If they became pregnant he turned them out without a penny but as Mary was already heavily pregnant she was safe from his advances. When her pains began she didn't know that the child was coming but Mrs Clark told her to hurry and get to the hospital right away because they didn't have a suitable bed for her at the inn. Mrs Clark helped Mary into a hackney coach and gave the coachman 4d, telling him to take Mary to the City Road Laying-in Hospital. As they drove along the roads the coachman begged Mary to hold on until they got there. They arrived just in time for the matron, Mrs Newby and several pupil midwives to deliver the baby, which was a boy. Mary stayed at the hospital for one week as a patient and then she worked there for a while as a servant. She then returned to Mrs Clark but the landlady said she could no longer employ her because she had a child, so Mary took lodgings in Charlotte Street and tried to get her baby into the Foundling Hospital. She told the administrators that she couldn't support him because his father had deserted them. She tried on three consecutive Wednesdays but the hospital was always full, but on the fourth Wednesday they had one space and Mary's baby was admitted.

She went back into service, this time at a Dancing Academy for Young Ladies. Once a week she went to see her child but he always looked very pale and weak. Mary didn't think that he was being very well looked after but there was nothing she could do about that. After being at the academy for two weeks she discovered a secret about one of the dance teachers. She promised to keep this secret but the head of the academy found out and both Mary and the teacher were dismissed. Later that same day she went to the Foundling Hospital to enquire about her son but was told that the child had died. He was only four months old but the cause of his death was not disclosed. Now in great need of comfort, Mary decided to go home to her mother. She had enough money for a coach from the Bull Inn at Aldgate Street but this was only to ride on top. That was the worst place to be on a coach for it was always cold and dangerous up there. The coachman was dressed in so many clothes that he could hardly move but that was the only way for him to keep warm on the journey. Mary wore as many clothes as she had and clung on to whatever she could so as not to fall off and possibly be killed.

When she arrived in Witheridge her mother was very sympathetic and her father, for the first time, treated her almost with respect. She stayed there for ten days but then decided to be on her way again. Her trunk of possessions was sent to Bristol by wagon while she set off to walk to Plymouth to try and earn some money. As it grew dark she became hungry and footsore and in need of rest. Then she saw some gypsies by the roadside so she stopped to warm herself by their fire. They felt sorry for her and gave her food and tea. The chief was called Rom Baro and he thought that Mary would be useful to them because she was quick to learn their ways. As this would be better than walking all the way to Plymouth, Mary decided to stay with the gypsies for a while. She went around with the women selling bunches of flowers and herbs and she also told fortunes finding it amusing that people believed what she said. The gypsies said that she could make a lot of money because she was cleaver as a fortune-teller. She picked up some of their language and also sang their songs and danced their gipsy dances. But Mary only stayed with the gypsies for three days and then left when they asked her to steal for them.

She then went across country to Teignmouth and from there to Honiton, acting all the way as a foreigner, begging at houses. When she had saved 10/- she got on a coach to Bristol. As soon as she arrived in this city she began to look for lodgings. She met a young woman named Eleanor Biggins who directed her to Mrs Neale's lodging house and here she stayed for nearly three weeks. One day, for a frolic, she and Eleanor dressed up as foreigners, Mary with a turban and Eleanor with a shawl and earrings. They went out into the streets begging and managed to earn 5/- to share between them. Mary spoke only in her foreign lingo and Eleanor pretended to be dumb. Everywhere they went they were taken for strangers newly arrived on a boat. The next day Mary had the idea of travelling far away to try and make her fortune and she made enquiries at the Quay to see if there was a vessel bound for America. One captain said he would take her for £5 and would be sailing in fifteen days. She decided that the only way she could obtain the money without the risk of being apprehended as a vagabond and sent to the House of Correction would be to dress as a foreigner and beg, her strange clothes and language protecting her from the law. She left her trunk at Mrs Neale's lodging house and said she would return to collect it and pay her arrears in a few days.

Dressed in her most unusual clothing she left the house with nothing but a bundle in which she carried some coins, a comb and a piece of soap. On her way from Bristol she buried her common clothes in a hole under a tree then headed for Lamplighter's Hall by Lord de Clifford's. She was constantly stopped on the road by people wanting to know who she was. Some gave her money and a farmer took her home to show to his wife. They fed her well and tried to communicate with her but they could not understand her language. They thought perhaps she was French and so they took her to a nearby house to meet the French cook. He made a great fuss of her but he couldn't understand her either and thought she was probably Spanish. One of the servants said she knew a Spanish woman in Bristol and would take her there immediately, but Mary didn't want to do that and she escaped out the door and ran over the fields and out of sight. Soon it started to pour with rain so she knocked on the door of a labourer's cottage and was invited in by the wife. She was allowed to stay for the night and was put up in the loft. In the morning she left the house and crossed the Marsh and on to Passage Road. Here she met a man who took her to the local village and then to a French governess at a nearby gentleman's house. The lady of the house was sure that

Mary was Spanish and gave her a letter of address to Charles Harvey, the French Consul in Queen Square, Bristol, who spoke Spanish well.

Thanking them with her hand-signs Mary left the house and continued on her way. As mid-day approached she sat to rest outside a public house. The owner and his wife, with the use of gestures, begged her to come inside. When Mary went in she met the man she had met earlier, who explained that he was a wheelwright's son. He insisted on accompanying Mary on the next part of her journey. He said he had been paid to do so by the French governess, so Mary was unable to get rid of him. As they walked back towards Bristol the man told Mary that he wanted her to meet a Spaniard that he knew living in the house of a Mr Mortimer in Clifton, but she made signs that she had to go to Queen Square. She didn't want to but there was no way of getting away from this man. When they reached the Square the man began to make enquires as to where the French Consul lived. He became so engrossed in his conversation that Mary took this opportunity to slip away unnoticed. She hid on the Quay until it was safe for her to leave and then she made her way north to Almondsbury. She took off her bonnet and put on her scarf as a turban. At Almondsbury Hill she went to a shoemaker's shop and asked for lodgings but the shoemaker didn't understand her and gave her some bread and butter.

He then took her to the home of Rev Hunt but the reverend was not at home. Mary gestured that she wanted to sleep there but Mrs Hunt didn't want her to do that and she sent for Mr Overton, the Poorhouse Overseer. When he arrived and saw the young woman he wasn't sure of what he should do and so he went to Knole Park, the home of Samuel and Elizabeth Worrall and told Mr Worrall of the young foreign woman who had been found wandering around in the village. So that is the story of how Mary Wilcox (or Wilcocks) who was also known as Mary Baker came into the lives of Mr and Mrs Worrall.

Although Samuel Worrall thought that Mary had made him and his wife a laughing-stock, Mrs Worrall felt sorry for her and said she would try to help. She arranged and paid for her passage to America (although it was only on a cargo ship) and she furnished Mary with clothes, money and food for the voyage to support her until she could find service in Philadelphia. She asked the captain and passengers to offer Mary their protection during the voyage and see that she came to no harm. She also had her name entered as Mary Burgess (a surname suggested by Mary herself) because now the names of Wilcocks and Baker were too well known. Mrs Worrall also insisted that Mary should "travel incognito for she may become conceited and play her part to the end." So Mary Wilcox left Almondsbury and sailed to Philadelphia on 18th June 1817 aboard the brig *Robert and Ann*, which carried a mixed cargo listed as "pig-iron, mallets, glass bottles, tobacco pipes, woollens, carpeting, cheese, tripe, a bedstead, two fouling-pieces and one chest of stationary together with Mary and several other passengers." Despite Mary's hoax, Mrs Worrall had become very fond of her and the strange way that she always pleased and entertained her and her husband, as well as all of their guests, and she was very sorry to see her go.

Soon after Mary had left for America, Captain Palmer told Mrs Worrall that he would investigate Mary's story to try and find out how much of it was true. He visited Mary's parents in Witheridge and then went to London to have a word with the people she said she had met there. What he found was that most of Mary's story was true although some of it was slightly exaggerated. He also discovered that all who came to know Mary quickly became very fond of her. She was always hard working and honest and no one ever spoke ill of her. But among the things that Captain Palmer found about Mary, which didn't quite tie in with her story, was that her child's father was not a sailor but the master of a family in whose service she had been employed somewhere in the country. She had been seduced by him and therefore left his employ. But whether or not this was true cannot be said for she also told some people that the father was a bricklayer. It was also impossible to say to whom, if anyone, she was married, or who the father of her child was, but she certainly *did* have a child. A Mrs Starling who employed Mary for a few weeks said that she found her to be charming but odd and eccentric. She told stories to Mrs Starling's children of gypsies and werewolves. She said that Mary, "could not be right in the head, and yet she charmed us all." Palmer also found that Mary was admitted to the Magdalene Hospital on 4th February 1813 under the name of Anne Burgess and said she was born on 11th November 1792.

Mary returned to England in 1820 and set herself up in Regent Street, Clifton, in a booth where she advertised herself as "*The Princess Caraboo.*" Unfortunately, very few people went to see her because by this time she had been very much forgotten. She gave up the booth and went to Bath to try her luck there but she found business in that city to be no better. Returning to Bristol she went to live in Bedminster where in 1849 she was living Under Pyle Hill. She made a living and supported her daughter (the father of whom is unknown) by selling leeches to the infirmary hospital.

Mary Wilcox, alias Mary Baker, alias Mary Burgess, alias Princess Caraboo, died in Bedminster on Christmas Eve, 1864. The location of her grave, thought to be somewhere in south Bristol, is unknown.

The Curse of Rebecca Berjew

In the late 1380s a man named Roger Berjew set up an apothecary shop at the bottom of High Street in Bristol and this started a long line of Berjew apothecaries that lasted for over four hundred years. In the early 1440s the business was being run by John Berjew who lived with his wife Alice in rooms above the apothecary shop. Towards the end of 1445 they had their first child, a daughter Alice who was named after the mother, and two years later they had a son whom they named Nathaniel. These were the first two of eleven children born to John and Alice Berjew.

When Alice, the daughter, was eighteen years old she married Robert Chester, a wealthy Bristol merchant who was many years her senior, but after three years Robert died leaving his fortune to his wife. At first she didn't know what to do with her money but Alice soon made up her mind to carry on her deceased husband's business and she became one of the few female merchants working in Bristol. She quickly became a very good businesswoman and was well liked and respected by the other merchants of the town. In 1470 she paid for the building of a crane on the Back to help with the loading and unloading of ships, and this became known as the Alice Chester Crane.

Back in the autumn of 1448 a young woman entered the apothecary shop and asked John Berjew if he could mix her a herbal remedy for severe headaches that she had been suffering from for several months. She said that she had been ten times to visit a haggard old woman who lived in a cottage in the Kingswood district; an area reputed as being the haunt of witches. The old hag, who said she had cures for every ailment under the sun, had been selling the young woman a potion made of herbs and certain animal parts that were boiled in a pot over her cottage fire. But these potions had only made the young woman feel worse so she decided to go to the apothecary instead.

John Berjew asked the woman a few questions about her headaches to see if he could discover the cause and then he mixed a remedy consisting of herbs alone. Three weeks later the woman returned to say that her headaches had gone and she purchased some more of the herbal mix, just in case they came back. The following week a haggard old woman came into the shop complaining that John Berjew had stolen one of her customers. This was the same old hag who had been treating the young woman for headaches. Berjew told her that her potion had been making the headaches worse because her so-called remedies were based on superstition rather than any medicinal knowledge. The old hag then became abusive and told Berjew that if he didn't stop stealing her customers she would make him very sorry.

"And what are you going to do?" asked Berjew. "There's nothing you can do, is there?"

The old hag replied, "I'll put a curse on you, that's what I'll do. I see that your wife is pregnant, but that baby will die within a year. Never again will you have a child that will live beyond infancy. This is the curse I place on you now – *This is the curse I place upon you. This is a curse that is to come true. To break the curse there's naught you can do. I place this curse upon John Berjew."*

The old hag turned and rushed out of the shop without waiting for a reply. John Berjew, being an apothecary, didn't believe in the power of witches' curses and preferred to trust in the natural remedies of nature. He told his wife not to worry and that everything was going to be well.

In the early spring the following year the baby was born but it died from a fever within a month. John told his wife that this was a natural death and had nothing to do with the curse. Two years later they had another baby but this one also died within a month. Over the following seventeen years they had six more babies but all of them died in infancy. Even after all these deaths John Berjew refused to believe that they had anything to do with the curse. His wife, however, was convinced that they had been caused by the words of the old hag and so, to show her that she was wrong, John decided to try a special diet and a herbal remedy that he had never tried before. Ten months later Alice became pregnant and she gave birth to a girl on New Years Day, 25th March 1470, a very special day in the medieval calendar. For three months Alice refused to give the baby a name, fearing that the child would not survive. However, the daughter turned out to be a strong and healthy baby and so, on Midsummer's Day, 24th June, the baby was christened and given the name of Rebecca.

Two years later John died of smallpox and his son Nathaniel took over the apothecary business. As Rebecca grew she became fascinated by Nathaniel's work and helped him to collect herbs and mix potions to cure people's ills. She learnt as much as she could and became so skilled and knowledgeable at the apothecaries art that by the age of ten she was almost as competent as Nathaniel himself. This, for a girl, was a dangerous thing because females with such skills were usually accused of being witches. Any woman who was tried and found guilty of witchcraft could be executed or whipped out of town. This meant that Rebecca had to be very careful and she only worked in the preparation room at the back of the shop. Here she sang songs as she went about here business, many of them being songs that she made up. Some of them were songs of love and some were about the things she had seen in nature, including songs to go with the potions she was mixing at the time. This was now becoming more dangerous than she realised because this was how witches chants and spells began. Nathaniel warned her not to be so foolish but Rebecca didn't see the harm in what she was doing and continued to make up her songs. It wasn't long before people coming into the shop began to hear these songs and although most of them thought it was charming to hear the singing of a young girl, some began to imagine there might be something more to it.

One day, in 1483, when Rebecca was thirteen years old, a young woman waited outside the shop until she saw Nathaniel leave. She then went inside to have a private word with Rebecca. She said that she had fallen in love with a handsome young seaman and wanted him to love her in return. But she didn't have much time to try and win his affections because he was soon to sail back to his homeport in Yorkshire. She asked Rebecca if she could mix her a love philtre to make the seaman fall for her and take her back to Yorkshire with him. Of course, a love philtre was not something that Rebecca had ever made and she didn't know if such a thing would be possible. But she was the sort of person who was willing to give it a try and she told the young woman (with some confidence) that she knew exactly what to do. The fact that she didn't wasn't going to stop her.

She took some dried parsley and crushed it into a powder. She then did the same with the dried leaves of sage and mixed the two together. Because she was trying to make a love potion she thought that it should smell nice and so she thought about adding some lavender, but that was too strong and too common for something as special as a love potion. Instead she took a sprig of dried rosemary, which still had its flowers, and crushed that into a powder together with a few leaves of dried lemon thyme. She put the powder mix into a small linen bag and cupped it in her hands as she said the words, "With parsley, sage, rosemary and thyme; the love of that man will soon be thine." She then gave the bag to the young woman and told her to go to the one she loved and stand about an arms length away from him. "When he's not looking, pour some of the powder into your hand and say the words, *With parsley, sage, rosemary and thyme, the love of that man will soon be mine.* Then blow the dust in his direction and wait to see what happens."

The woman left the shop and that was the last Rebecca saw of her until about a year later when, one afternoon, the woman came back into the shop looking very sad and downhearted. She told Rebecca that her love philtre and chant had worked and that her true love had taken her back to his home in Yorkshire where they were to be married. But she wanted to be honest with him and two days before the wedding she told him what she had done. However, this made him so angry that he called her a witch and refused to marry her and he turned her away with nothing more than the clothes that she wore. When she walked back into the apothecary shop she was still wearing the plain cameryk dress that she was to have been married in. Later the story of the young woman's spell was spread around the seaman's community in Yorkshire and from this has come the well-known folk song we know today as *Scarborough Fair*.

The story also spread among the people of Bristol but because Rebecca was so young (and was the sister of the apothecary) no one accused her of being a witch, although some people had their suspicions. Rebecca decided that it would be for the best if she didn't sing any more songs or make up any more rhymes for people to hear. She kept very quiet after that until one day, about five years later, the son of a merchant came into the shop. He was young and hansom and had something about him that Rebecca was very much attracted to. It wasn't love (at least not for what she saw) but something much deeper. Surface love is not true love – Rebecca knew that. She knew that true love only comes from deep within.

It was six months before Rebecca saw him again and this time the feeling within her was much stronger than it had been before. She began to think that perhaps this really could be true love and she also had a strange feeling that he felt the same about her. It just needed to be brought out, but as he was from a merchant family and she was only the sister of an apothecary, a relationship between them was never likely to happen. Several more months passed before she saw him again, this time at the Back where he was talking to a quay-porter about a ship's cargo. When he had gone she asked the labourer who the merchant was. He told Rebecca that his name was John, the son of the merchant Robert Strange.

Rebecca now began to wonder if her love potion would work for her as it had for the young woman she had helped seven years earlier. She made the same mix of parsley, sage, rosemary and thyme and wrapped it in a small linen bag. She carried this with her everywhere she went, using it as a pomander against the stench of the town. This way no one would question her about what it was and why she was carrying it. But Rebecca knew that she needed to have the mixture with her ready for the next time she saw John Strange because she had no idea when that might be.

She frequently walked the streets hoping to see him and she went to all the places where she thought he might be but as the months went by there was never any sign of him. Rebecca renewed her mixture every month but after a year there was still no sign of the man she had come to love. Then she discovered that he had gone to Spain for three years to work with John Thorne, a Bristol merchant who had just been made the Pilot Major of that country. Rebecca was devastated by this news but she was prepared to wait because she knew he would return one day. She only hoped that when he did he was still unwed and not taken up with a Spanish lady.

It was in the winter of 1495 (when Nathaniel and Rebecca Berjew were at the Back collecting some newly arrived sacks of Mediterranean herbs from Spain) that John Strange returned to Bristol. He had sailed aboard the same ship that had brought the sacks of herbs. He was with Robert Thorne and Hugh Elyot, two of Bristol's leading merchants, and with them was an Italian family who had been living in Valencia. The head of this family was a Genoese adventurer and one time spice merchant named Giovanni Caboto. He was accompanied by his wife Mattea and their three sons Lewis, Sebastian and Sancio, but during the time that Giovanni Caboto was in Bristol his name was anglicised to John Cabot.

Rebecca now had the chance that she had been waiting for. Her pomander was tied to her belt because she never went anywhere without it. Having helped Nathaniel to load the sacks onto a dogcart she left him to take the herbs back to the shop on his own. She then took a small amount of the herbal mix out of her pomander and held it in her hand as she walked up behind John Strange. When no one was looking she whispered the words, "With parsley, sage, rosemary and thyme; the love of John Strange will soon be mine." She then blew the dust in his direction and waited to see what would happen.

A moment later John turned round and as he caught sight of Rebecca he gave a look of surprise. "I remember you," he said. "You're Rebecca Berjew, the apothecary's sister." Rebecca could hardly believe that he remembered her. She just stood in shock not knowing what to say. John told her that he had some business to attend to at that moment but he hoped to see her again soon. Rebecca was stunned as she watched him walk away but now she really did believe that she had the power to cast magic spells.

Two days later Rebecca was working in the shop when John came in to see her. This was not to purchase a herbal remedy; he just wanted to know more about her. Although he was one of the merchant class and would have been expected to marry a merchant's daughter, the sister of an apothecary was also considered to be a suitable wife for a man of his standing. There was also the fact that as Rebecca's sister had married a merchant and had now become a merchant herself; this made Rebecca all the more acceptable to a merchant family. There was no talk of marriage of course, but John had become beguiled by the beautiful Rebecca Berjew. Over the following weeks they began to see more of each other, often going on walks along the Red Causeway at the northern end of the Avon Marsh. Here it was quiet where few people went so they were able to talk freely about all manner of things as they began to learn more about each other. But knowing what had happened to the young woman she first made the love potion for, Rebecca was not going to make the same mistake and she kept the potion and chant a secret from everyone.

Then one day in February John told Rebecca that he was going to London and would be away for about two weeks. He said he was going with Robert Thorne and Hugh Elyot to take the Italian John Cabot to see the king. The purpose of the visit was so that Cabot could petition the king for a licence to sail to the New World to claim that land for the English. Nineteen years earlier, in 1477, Thorne and Elyot had discovered that land when searching for new fishing grounds. But they were not permitted to use the land without permission from the king and so they petitioned him for a licence called letters patent. However, the king (Edward IV) refused, saying that he didn't want his merchants sailing on what he believed would be unprofitable expeditions. This angered Thorne and Elyot and so they began to use those lands illegally. They sent out four or five ships each year to the region that was referred to as Thorne's Land (now called Nova Scotia) with their ships returning to Bristol with huge catches of fish. Some of it was sold in the local markets but most of the fish was sold to the merchants of Spain and Portugal. But because they were using the lands illegally the business had to be kept a secret and this is the reason why the Bristol merchants were never credited with the discovery of the New World.

When Henry VII became King of England in 1485 he quickly developed a great suspicion about the dealings of the Bristol merchants. Because their fishing voyages were being carried out in such secrecy they were not declaring them and so were not paying any customs duty on their catches of fish. They would therefore have been in serious trouble with the king if he had known and so they had to be very careful. The king was so suspicious that he paid two visits to Bristol to check on the situation for himself. He guessed that something illegal was going on but he didn't know what. On his second visit he decided to punish the merchants just in case and he demanded a payment of £500 to be paid into the Royal Purse from the Bristol Custom's Revenue. He also levied a tax of £1 on every man who was worth more than £200 because, he said, "Their wives went so sumptuously apparelled."

It became even worse for the merchants when, in 1494, the Spanish and the Portuguese (who were beginning to make discoveries of lands beyond Europe) came to an agreement between themselves declaring that all newly discovered lands should belong to them alone. The treaty was sanctioned by the Pope and this meant that the Spanish were given the right to claim all the lands of the New World. The Bristol merchants were now in danger of losing their fishing grounds and they had no alternative but to make a new petition to claim their lands for England. But because they had been using those lands illegally for many years they had to be very careful about how they approached the king.

It was for this reason that they employed a foreigner, the Italian adventurer John Cabot to petition the king on their behalf. They told him to inform the king that he wanted to go in search of "previously unknown lands," and to claim those lands for England. After giving the matter some thought, the king decided to grant the licence but he told Cabot that he must not sail to any unknown lands to the south of the line of latitude at the southernmost part of the English mainland.

The preparations were made and in May 1497 Robert Thorne and Hugh Elyot set sail from Bristol aboard Thorne's ship the *Matthew* taking Cabot to claim their New Found Land. Although Cabot was little more than a passenger on this voyage, Thorne pretended that Cabot was in command so as to avoid any trouble with the king. In reality this was just another Bristol fishing trip and Thorne, Elyot and the entire crew knew exactly where they were going. Cabot was the only person aboard the *Matthew* who hadn't been to the New World before.

When they returned three months later they went to see the king who was delighted with, what he believed to be a wonderful new discovery. He granted Cabot another licence to extend the discoveries and he also gave him a reward of £10, an annual pension of £20, and the title of Grand Admiral. With his newly acquired fame and fortune he bought himself the most elaborate costume he could find and returned to Bristol to show himself off to all the townsfolk. The news that he had discovered the New Found Land and claimed that land for England had quickly spread and all the people who didn't know the truth were anxiously waiting to see him and to welcome him home as a hero.

Those who *did* know the truth, such as the merchants and their seamen, were not able to say anything because they still needed to keep their secret. But Cabot began to strut around the streets of Bristol showing off and bragging about his great discovery knowing full well that no one was likely to contradict him. Soon his arrogant manner started to annoy and anger many of those who did know the truth. Some of them asked Cabot to stop his disgraceful behaviour but the Italian's head was too full of conceit and he continued to brag and boast even more.

When John Strange informed Rebecca of the true sequence of events it made her want to do something to stop Cabot from bragging about an achievement that wasn't his own. She thought about mixing a potion to blow at him together with a small rhyme or chant. But that would have been too dangerous because Cabot was always surrounded by people and she would certainly have been seen. She would then have been accused of being a witch and that could have led to her execution. She had to think of another way but try as she did she couldn't think of anything.

As the weeks went by the merchants and their seamen became even more angered by Cabot's actions but the more they asked him to stop lying and showing off to the townsfolk the more he continued. Then one day Rebecca saw him walking out of Nicholas Street on to High Street just opposite the apothecary's shop. She pushed her way through the crowd that was surrounding him and went up to Cabot and accused him of being a liar and a cheat. The crowd was stunned into almost complete silence because they all knew and respected Nathaniel and Rebecca Berjew and any such statement from either of them would never be made without cause. Cabot just looked at her with a cold stare and said how dare she accuse him of such things. But Rebecca told him that she knew the truth and that he was a terrible person to be deceiving the good and innocent townspeople in such a way.

An argument then broke out between them and Cabot told Rebecca to go away and stop trying to cause trouble for him. But Rebecca told Cabot quite firmly that he, as a foreigner, is the one who should go away. Cabot angrily replied that he was not going anywhere because Bristol was now his home and he was the greatest hero that Bristol ever had. This remark made Rebecca really angry and without stopping to think about what she was saying she replied, "Then I curse you John Cabot for treating my friends and the people of Bristol as gullible fools. They do not deserve to be treated this way by any outsider. You are the one who should leave this town and never come back. I tell you now that the next voyage you make from this port will be your last and you will never return here again. In addition to this, the name of Cabot will forever be cursed in Bristol."

The townspeople now began to feel very confused. Was Rebecca right they wondered? The story soon spread around the town, causing most of the people to stop chasing after Cabot as if he were someone special. His popularity had taken quite a knock but he didn't care too much about that. He had a new licence for a voyage back to the New World and the preparations were already well under way. This time he would be sailing with five ships on an expedition to try and reach Cathay and the Spice Islands that were thought to be no more than a few hundred miles beyond the islands of the New World. Of course, no one knew that the land was not a group of islands but a vast continent, but Cabot knew that if he could reach the Orient then he would have a legitimate claim to be called a hero.

The following May the Cabot fleet of five Bristol ships set sail from the Back. As they were crossing the Sea of Darkness (the North Atlantic Ocean) they ran into a very bad storm. One of the ships was damaged and put into an Irish port for repairs before returning to Bristol but the other four ships continued on their way – and disappeared forever. The ships' owners waited in vain for their vessels to return, but none of them ever did.

After two years, many of the townspeople began to talk about the curse of Rebecca Berjew and wondered if she really had condemned John Cabot to doom. There was also talk about the possibility of her being a witch and using magic spells to back up her curse. The rumours spread to such an extent that Rebecca was summoned before a council of merchants held in the Guild Hall. If she were found guilty of witchcraft then she would be sentenced to death or stripped to the waist and whipped out of town, never being allowed to return.

None of the merchants at Rebecca's trial believed her to be guilty and what she had said about Cabot they knew to be true. Thorne and Elyot were especially disappointed with Cabot and they spoke in Rebecca's defence saying that Cabot really was a liar who had deliberately deceived the people of the town. But other members of the merchant council said that she had made matters worse for herself by cursing Cabot and his name. The fact that her words had come true would show in the eyes of many that she was a witch with genuine magical powers. For this reason, those who considered her guilty would want to see that justice was done and a punishment carried out.

Then John Strange stood up and said that if Rebecca were a respectable member of a merchant family no one would accuse her of being a witch because witches are all of a common or lowly type. Everyone knew this to be true and everyone knew that Rebecca was a respectable and well-loved member of the community. But if she became the wife of a Bristol merchant, as did her sister, then everyone would know that Rebecca was certainly not a witch. Then, in front of all the merchants present, John asked Rebecca to marry him.

The love spell she had started to use on John Strange five years earlier, and had continued to use ever since, had now brought her what she desired. It didn't matter to Rebecca that this might have happened anyway, she had got what she most wanted in life. She immediately accepted John's proposal and a marriage between them was arranged to take place as quickly as possible. When it was announced to the townspeople one week later that Rebecca was now married to the merchant John Strange, no one looked upon her as a witch any longer.

As for the curse that she placed on John Cabot saying that he and the name of Cabot will forever be cursed in Bristol, perhaps there *was* something in this. Perhaps Rebecca really did have a strange magical power because Cabot's pension, which was paid to his wife Mattea in 1499 in his absence, was stopped when Cabot didn't return. Without her husband's pension to support her, Mattea found it difficult to provide for herself and her children. Her middle son, Sebastian, who was an adventurous eleven-year-old, went out one day and stole three loaves of bread but unfortunately for him he was caught and reported to the town sheriff. He was sentenced to one year in jail but the following week, just before Sebastian was to be taken to the Newgate Prison to begin his sentence, Mattea secured a passage for herself and her three sons on a ship bound for their homeport of Venice in Italy.

On the morning the ship was due to depart Mattea and her sons walked down to the Back to board the waiting ship. She was wearing her mourning clothes, which were in the late 15th century Venetian style of a dark purple-blue dress and tricornis mourning cap from beneath which a veil hung down over her face and pulled around over her left shoulder. Just as they were about to board the ship the authorities arrived to take Sebastian into custody. He struggled to try and get away but being rather small for his age one of the men easily picked him up and carried him away under his arm with his head facing back. Mattea knew there was nothing she could do but to stand on the quay and watch her son being taken out of her sight. Sebastian reached out his arms towards his mother and cried a pitiful wailing cry. Mattea called after him, promising to send him money for his passage home as soon as he was free, but that was all she could do.

When Sebastian left prison one year later, instead of sailing back to Italy he decided to remain in Bristol and try to get employment with one of the local merchants. He went back to the house where his family had been living in Nicholas Street but this was now occupied by another family. (On the site of this house there now stands a building called the Gresham Chambers. Built in 1868 it is in the Venetian Gothic Revival style and has four sculpted heads across its façade. One of these is the famous *Veiled Lady* wearing the headdress of the late 15th century Venetian woman's mourning attire).

Sebastian now went to stay with the family of a friend who lived in a house at the Corn Street end of Nicholas Street. He soon gained employment with the merchant John Jay and worked his way up to become a sea captain by the time he was in his early twenties. But it seems that the curse of Rebecca Berjew was still upon him for he frequently met with misfortune throughout his life. To try and improve his standing in the community he often told lies about his achievements. He claimed that he had sailed on the 1497 voyage with his father and told everyone that he was a true Bristolian saying that he had been born in this town. Through his lies he eventually managed to get financial backing for a voyage to try and find a northwest passage to the Orient. He reached the coast of what is now known as Labrador and he sailed as far as the bay, which was later named Hudson Bay, but this voyage ended in failure. The provisions ran low and the ship started to leak. When Cabot said he wanted to continue, the crew rebelled against him and forced him to sail back to Bristol.

When he returned he was informed that Henry VII had died and the new king, Henry VIII was not interested in his schemes. Unhappy about this situation Cabot transferred his allegiance to the Castilian service. In the employ of the Spanish he led an expedition to Brazil to explore the coast but instead of exploring he ignored his orders and spent the next five years in what turned out to be a fruitless search for silver. When he returned to Spain he was arrested and banished to Africa as a punishment. He was later pardoned but instead of going back to work for the Spanish, he returned to England. King Philip was furious and ordered him to return to Spain; but Cabot refused. However, when Philip married Queen Mary of England and came to this country in 1557 he immediately ordered that Cabot be deprived of half his pension.

So whether Rebecca's curse was genuine or not it certainly had the desired effect. What she said about John Cabot never returning from his next voyage was correct. Her statement that the name of Cabot would be cursed in Bristol also proved to be true. But just how long will this curse last. Certainly there have been many Cabot mishaps, even into the 21st century. To mark the 400th anniversary of Cabot's claiming of the New World a tower was built on Brandon Hill. Due to be opened on the anniversary date of 24th June 1897 it was not until that date that the foundation stone was eventually laid. During the construction two workmen were injured and another almost killed by a piece of falling masonry. The tower was eventually completed and opened on 6th September 1898, just over 14 months late.

To mark the 500th anniversary of Cabot's voyage a representative late 15th century caravel was built and sailed to America. During the sea trials one of the crew was badly injured and had to be air lifted off the ship and flown to hospital for emergency treatment. The voyage to America went well enough but there was one mishap when the ship ran aground in the Saint Lawrence River and got stuck in the mud. Then early in 2007 the *Matthew* sailed from

Bristol to Cardiff. After a short stay the crew left Cardiff Harbour in the evening and made their way into the Bristol Channel just before nightfall. After four hours of sailing most of the crew had retired for the night leaving only the helmsman and navigator on duty. Suddenly there was a tremendous thud as the ship came to an abrupt halt and rolled violently to port before resuming forward motion. Obviously they had struck something very big and the crew rushed to see what had happened. The navigator had left the deck to go to the navigation cabin to check their position leaving the helmsman alone on the whipstaff. As it was a clear calm night with only light winds and a slight swell, they were not expecting any trouble, but suddenly an anchored lightship came in to view as if out of nowhere. It should have been clearly seen and heard because it had a bright light flashing on top and a loud bell ringing three times every minute. The helmsman only saw it when it was just a few hundred yards away and he pushed the whipstaff hard to port to try and avoid it. For some reason the ship did not respond and continued on a straight course, crashing into the lightship head on and destroying the figurehead. This diverted the ship to port but the hull of the *Matthew* hit the ship and damaged some of the lower starboard planks. But it was not as bad as it might have been. Another foot lower and the *Matthew* could have been holed at the waterline and sunk, possibly with the loss of several lives.

A few months later, at the end of September 2007, the Cabot Tower developed some large cracks and had to be closed to the public. Repairs were needed before it was too late and the tower came crashing down. Not long after that, down at the new Bristol Shopping Centre (which had been named *Cabot* Circus) a large panel fell from one of the buildings narrowly missing a woman pedestrian. She could easily have been killed. A few weeks later, at this same Cabot shopping centre, a glass door shattered and fell onto a small baby in a pushchair. That baby almost lost an eye.

So it seems that the curse on the name of Cabot is still with us and all this because of the arrogance and bragging of the Italian adventurer who was only brought to Bristol to help the merchants hide their secret and illegal activities. This Italian was only in Bristol for just over two years but in that time he turned many Bristolians against him. But whether you believe in curses or not, some of them do come true so perhaps you would do well never to forget – the curse of Rebecca Berjew.

The Illustrations and Photographs

Page 7
The Kinsale Giant, Patrick Cotter O'Brien in 1780, aged 20 when he was about 8'3" tall. The picture is adapted from contemporary drawings with a man (5'6") and a woman (5'2") drawn to the same scale. These were the average heights of men and women in the 1780s,two inches shorter than they were by 1980.

Page 11
Typical scene of an annual fair of the type held in many towns and cities throughout the country.

Page 14
Whiteladies Road branched off the Clifton Road by Tyndall Park and extended to the White Ladies Tavern at the foot of the hill, which became known as Blackboy Hill.
In the illustration the Blackamoor's Head is drawn from old photographs but the White Ladies Tavern is drawn from imagination because no picture of it is known to exist.

Page 17
Drawing of Cook's Folly from old photographs.

Page 18
Avalon and Vincent who lived at a time when giants in excess of 20 feet in height dwelt in the lands of northwest Europe.
Drawing is adapted from illustrations by Huard in *Heroes of Asgard*, 1872.

Page 21
Photograph of the statue of Sabrina, which is a part of the Fountain of Sabrina located behind Broad Quay House on Bristol's city centre.
The background is a pencil sketch of the river that took her life.

Page 25

Photograph of the Veiled Lady, one of four sculptured heads supposed to be representing the four seasons. They are on the façade of the Gresham Chambers at 18, St Nicholas Street, Bristol. This building was designed by the architects Ponton and Gough in the Venetian Gothic Revival style and erected in 1868.

The heads are unusual in as much as the Veiled Lady is in the position of autumn and this should be represented by a middle-aged woman with harvest corn in her hair.

The Veiled lady should not be there.

Page 28

The head and shoulders of Princess Caraboo drawn from contemporary paintings. This is very much how she would have looked when she first appeared in Almondsbury in 1817.

Page 39

Sketch of Princess Caraboo in the costume she designed and made herself.

Page 60

Rebecca Berjew. There are no known drawings or paintings of Rebecca but there are a few brief descriptions. She had long dark hair and large sparkling eyes. Her complexion was soft and she had an enchanting smile.

Front Cover

Sketch coloured in pastels depicting images from some of the tales.